THE USES OF AIR PHOTOGRAPHY

THE USES OF AIR PHOTOGRAPHY
Nature and Man in a New Perspective

Edited by **J. K. S. St Joseph**

Director in Aerial Photography in the University of Cambridge

With contributions by
Lord Esher, F. Fraser Darling, R. W. Hey,
M. D. Knowles, J. Milton, R. M. S. Perrin,
C. D. Pigott, J. Rishbeth, Sir Ian Richmond,
J. K. S. St Joseph, J. A. Steers,
R. M. Watson, W. W. Williams

THE JOHN DAY COMPANY, NEW YORK

FOREWORD

by The Chairman of the Committee for Aerial Photography

RECOGNITION of the value of air photography as a medium for teaching and research in many different disciplines led the University of Cambridge, in 1949, to constitute a Committee to promote the further development of the subject. A year earlier Dr J. K. S. St Joseph had been appointed the first Curator in Aerial Photography, a post which in due course came under the general direction of the Committee. From its inception the Committee has deliberately sponsored annual programmes of reconnaissance: indeed, the principal distinguishing feature of the Cambridge Collection is that the photographs come from flights specifically planned for research. At first the Collection of photographs was housed in a small room in the Museum of Classical Archaeology. Growth was so rapid that a move had to be made to separate premises in 1953; now further accommodation is again needed.

All the photographs in the Collection have been taken by the Curator: until 1958 the flying facilities were largely provided by the Royal Air Force during training flights. It is a pleasure to take this opportunity of acknowledging the great debt that the Committee owes to the Air Ministry for making this possible. More recently, the progressive withdrawal from Service use of slow-flying aircraft suitable for the work made it evident that the Committee should operate its own aircraft. A generous grant from the Nuffield Foundation in 1960 enabled the Committee to purchase an Auster aircraft and to enlist the services of Squadron Leader A. G. Douglass as pilot. In 1962 the increasing value of the Committee's work in the University was recognised by the conversion of the office of Curator to that of Director and, three years later, there was established a Senior Assistantship in Research in Aerial Photography, to which Mr D. R. Wilson was appointed.

The extension of the Committee's work soon outgrew the possibilities of an Auster and, in 1965, the University purchased a twin-engined Cessna Skymaster aircraft as a replacement. This machine is well equipped for widely ranging reconnaissance flights over any part of the British Isles and is suitable for vertical photography with a photogrammetric camera. Vertical photographs can now be taken of small selected areas at frequent intervals, so that comparatively rapid changes in the landscape may be accurately recorded, a service of great value in many fields of research.

The number of photographs in the Cambridge Collection steadily grows and their use by various Faculties of the University for teaching and research is ever increasing. The organisation has in fact become a service department for the University. In addition, there is a continual growing demand for photographs from institutions and scholars outside Cambridge—a demand by no means easy to satisfy with our present limited staff and accommodation.

Many photographs from the Cambridge Collection have been published in books and learned journals. While these are often of specialised interest to the scholar and the research student, they hardly provide a general picture of the development of the subject. This book, largely written by members of the Committee, affords some account of the present varied applications of air photography, and incidentally, of the scope and nature of the Committee's work. It is fitting to record here that the work owes much to the Committee's first Chairman—Dr H. Hamshaw Thomas, F.R.S., himself a pioneer in the use of air photographs in the War of 1914-18.

Committee for Aerial Photography,   J. A. STEERS
Sidgwick Avenue,
Cambridge
December 1965

CONTRIBUTORS

LORD ESHER, President of the Royal Institute of British Architects.

F. FRASER DARLING, The Conservation Foundation, New York.

R. W. HEY, Lecturer in Geology in the University of Cambridge and Fellow of Churchill College.

M. D. KNOWLES, Regius Professor Emeritus of Modern History in the University of Cambridge and Fellow of Peterhouse.

J. MILTON, The Conservation Foundation, New York.

R. M. S. PERRIN, Lecturer in Soil Science in the University of Cambridge.

C. D. PIGOTT, Professor of Biology in the University of Lancaster.

J. RISHBETH, Lecturer in Botany in the University of Cambridge and Fellow of Corpus Christi College.

The late SIR IAN RICHMOND, Professor of the Archaeology of the Roman Empire in the University of Oxford and Fellow of All Souls College. President of the Society of Antiquaries.

J. K. S. ST JOSEPH, Director in Aerial Photography in the University of Cambridge and Fellow of Selwyn College.

J. A. STEERS, Professor of Geography in the University of Cambridge and Fellow of St Catharines College.

R. M. WATSON, Serengeti Research Project, Tanzania National Parks.

W. W. WILLIAMS, Lecturer in Geography in the University of Cambridge and Fellow of Fitzwilliam House.

CONTENTS

Note. In the description of the plates, the reference number of the particular photograph, the date of photography, and, for vertical photographs, the approximate scale, is given whenever known. References in the form of one or more letters followed by one or more (usually two) digits are to photographs in the Cambridge University Collection. The source of the remaining photographs can be obtained by referring to the acknowledgements (p. 12).

For photographs over Britain the normal National Grid reference of the feature in question is printed within brackets after the place-name or county. The National Grid, now included on all official maps of the Ordnance Survey, provides a single reference system for the whole country. Each 100-kilometre square of the grid is denoted by a pair of letters. Any point within one of these squares can be located to the nearest 100 metres by a six-figure reference, in which three digits indicating 'eastings' are followed by three digits indicating 'northings'.

Notes to the text are printed at the end of the chapter to which they belong. The selected bibliography at the end of Chapter VIII has been included as a guide to the use being made of air photography for conservation and census of many different species of animals.

LIST OF PLATES

ACKNOWLEDGEMENTS

Plates 9, 15, 16, 18, 27a,b, 41a, are Royal Air Force official photographs and thus British Crown Copyright. They are published by permission of the Ministry of Defence (Air). In addition, for Plate 15 the Commissioner of Lands, Aden, has granted permission for publication, and for Plate 16 the Surveyor-General, Ministry of Land and Natural Resources, Zambia, similarly. Plate 17 which is the copyright of the Government of Kenya, is published by permission of the Director of Surveys, Kenya: Plate 31 is reproduced by permission of the Government of Tanzania. Plates 29 and 30 are published by permission of Fairey Surveys Ltd: Plate 14 by permission of Ambassador Irish Oil Co.: Plate 46, taken by Aero Photo Inc., Quebec, was kindly supplied by Dr D. E. Sergeant, of the Fisheries Research Board of Canada, and is reproduced by permission of that Board: Plate 45 is by permission of the National Parks Branch of the Department of Northern Affairs and National Resources, Canada: Plates 43-4, kindly supplied by Dr M. Cowie, Director of the Kenya National Parks, are reproduced by permission of Dr Glover: Plate 38 is by permission of Mr C. V. Dadd: Plates 48, 49b are by Mr M. I. M. Turner, Park Warden, Kenya National Parks: Plates 49a, 50-2 are by Mr R. M. Watson. Plates 1-7, 10-13, 19-26, 28, 32-7, 39, 40a,b, 41b, 42, 53-61, 63-5, 67-84 are from the Cambridge University Collection, and were taken by Dr J. K. S. St Joseph. Of these, Plates 1, 2, 5, 6, 13, 20-5, 36, 39, 41b, 53, 54, 56, 60-1, 63, 67, 68, 71, 72, 74-7, and 81 are British Crown Copyright; the remainder are the copyright of the University of Cambridge. Plate 62 is published by permission of the Librarian, All Souls College, Oxford: plate 66 by permission of the Marquess of Hertford.

Plate 1.   The Dovey valley

J. K. S. St JOSEPH

The Scope of Air Photography

MORE than a century has passed since the first air photographs were taken from a balloon over Paris,[1] but for many years, until about 1914, such photographs were so rare that they were regarded as curiosities. The half-century between then and now has seen the development of air photography into an instrument of precision used for survey and research the world over, while in recent years photography from artificial satellites has afforded possibilities of recording on a few photographs whole continents, or the cloud-systems that cover them. The immense growth of the subject has been made possible both by the development of modern aircraft and by continued improvement in cameras, in lenses and in film, specially designed for air survey. About the beginning of the First World War, wooden box-cameras and glass plates were used, with provision for an observer to change plates while in the air. Today, the use of electrically-driven, remote-controlled roll-film cameras yields air photographs in numbers hardly dreamed of a generation ago, while the development of precision instruments for preparing accurate contoured maps from overlapping vertical photographs has provided a new means for the survey of large and inaccessible areas.

A map shows selected and conventionalised features: an air photograph makes no selection and employs no convention. A photograph will thus record not only such major features as are commonly delineated on a map, but a wealth of minor and often transient detail never found on the largest general survey. This detail constitutes an almost inexhaustible store of information of value to geology, to geography, to ecology, to agriculture, archaeology, history and town-planning; and these are only the principal fields of study that gain from the application of air photography to their problems. The extent of the help varies in different disciplines: the best results are obtained when the photography is carefully planned in regard to the problems awaiting solution. Thus, high-altitude vertical photographs in overlapping series may be required for regional survey, for general study of land use, or for geology, while low-level oblique photographs may prove best to record the past and present activities of man where these have intensively fashioned and scarred the face of the land. The fact that, compared with maps, photographs neither select nor conventionalise the information they present has called for special techniques of interpretation to serve this multiplicity of interests.

The work of interpretation, developed to a high degree of ingenuity and skill, has served the needs of military reconnaissance in two World Wars,[2] when under stress of national necessity great advances were made in the design both of cameras and of suitable aircraft to carry them. In peacetime these same skills can be harnessed to record the activities, large or small, of Nature, or of man, on the earth's surface.

Today the value of air photography, linked to adequate control-points on the ground, for detailed and rapid survey of remote, unmapped regions is widely acknowledged by all involved in such affairs. The method has long served official departments or commercial firms concerned with the use of land and the exploitation of natural resources in wide variety. Moreover, when evidence derived from air reconnaissance is combined with information yielded by other methods of survey, as to variations in the earth's gravitational or magnetic field such knowledge becomes of the greatest value in assessing the geological nature and structure of rocks comprising the upper part of the earth's

Plate 1. The Dovey valley, Merionethshire, looking north (foreground at SH844100). This panorama of the upper Dovey valley brings out, as in a model, the relief of the country in ridges and overlapping spurs, formed by winding upland streams. The contrast between enclosed fields in the valleys and the uncultivated moorland slopes can be readily appreciated. The triple summits of the Arans appear on the central skyline.

PZ 60   *24 June 1955*

crust. The photographic 'coverage' that has accumulated over several decades as a result of such air surveys in many different parts of the world, increasing in amount year by year, is to be found in the various collections of air photographs maintained by Government agencies and commercial firms. Very often the photographs have a value far wider than the immediate purpose for which they were taken, and strong arguments might be advanced for the preparation of a systematic guide or catalogue to all such existing material. Few countries, in fact, possess established national collections of air photographs with adequate facilities for study and research.

The large photographic collections already mentioned comprise, in the main, 'cover' obtained in the course of regional survey, when the requirement may involve flying with great precision on predetermined heights and courses to yield vertical photographs in single or overlapping series often at a relatively small scale. The photographs in the Cambridge University Collection are in complete contrast: they comprise both oblique and vertical photographs, taken from a light aircraft at a comparatively low altitude in the course of flights carefully planned, within the limited resources available, to meet special needs of teaching and research. These flights have ranged widely over the United Kingdom and Eire. Almost the whole of the United Kingdom had already been photographed from the air, either by the Royal Air Force, or by survey firms, much of it time and again, and the question may well be asked, if such extensive vertical 'cover' already exists, what need is there for further photographs? Vertical photographs taken from a high altitude to meet the needs of regional planning may under favourable conditions also serve geological studies and provide the botanist with surveys of contrasting types of vegetation. However, so intensive has the use of land become over large areas of the earth's surface that very great value may be derived from photography planned in regard to the solution of particular problems. This may involve photography at a large scale, under carefully chosen conditions of lighting, or at a particular season of the year. No regional survey can possibly meet all the specialised needs of those concerned with ever-varying natural conditions like coastal erosion and deposition, the study of plant diseases, detailed ecology, or the habits of wild animals, which may respectively call for photographs taken with regard to tidal conditions, or to the season and the state of growth of vegetation. The needs of architects, archaeologists and historians also involve special considerations of weather and lighting. Photographs that become available as a result of regional survey often prompt further studies of the kind already

mentioned, while there is no doubt that the scope for such work is increasing—both for general survey, as man's need to search for natural resources spreads ever more widely over the earth's surface, and for detailed survey to aid those concerned with innumerable aspects of the development of landscape by Nature and its use by man.

The land surface of the United Kingdom and Eire is unusually favourable for such studies. It includes a greater range and diversity of geographical and geological features and processes than almost any other part of the earth's surface of comparable size, even though their scale may be far smaller than in continental areas. This diversity of geology is reflected in a wide range of soils supporting correspondingly varied vegetation, a fact not always appreciated, but essential to our understanding of the infinitely varied natural background to human settlement in these islands. It provides also a clue to the many regional differences in the character of settlement in prehistoric and historic times. The patch-work nature of that settlement, evolved over centuries, is responsible for the moulding of the earth's surface by generations of human endeavour into a landscape which possesses not only a beauty associated with long and slow development, but an inexhaustible store of information about many kinds of human activities. Constructions of one age are often overlain, modified or erased by the work of another. Remains of many different ages may be found in those regions occupied by mankind for long periods, and the temperate climatic zone of north-west Europe offers remarkable opportunities for their study. The long succession of human invasions that have swept westward across Europe to these islands, the varied natural environment, the present wide extent of arable land on which vegetation responds in sensitive fashion to buried features in the soil, all combine to promote exceptionally favourable conditions for the study of history from the air.

The chapters that follow, most of them by members of the Cambridge Committee for Aerial Photography, describe some of the principal applications of this relatively new method of research. That many of

---

Plate 2.   Grib Gôch, Caernarvonshire (SH622552). The view is to the west-south-west with the summit of Snowdon just beyond the top right-hand corner. The photograph gives a spectacular view of the great corries and sharp arêtes eroded by ice in this group of mountains. The region is largely composed of varied volcanic rocks of Ordovician age, some of which (the calcareous volcanic ashes) support an interesting arctic-alpine flora. Part of the corrie-lake Glaslyn is just visible half-way up the left-hand margin. SM 16   *26 May 1956*

Plate 2. Grib Gôch

the plates are photographs of the United Kingdom, arises from the fact that the material in the Cambridge Collection is conveniently to hand. Most of the topics discussed could well have been illustrated by photographs from elsewhere, while certain applications of air photography, namely for animal counts, for regional surveys of special types of landscape or vegetation, or for the study of existing glaciers and ice-caps, cannot in the nature of things be illustrated in Britain. Photographs from other sources have thus been drawn upon, particularly high-altitude vertical 'cover', which is not included in the Cambridge Collection. In this introductory chapter, some account must be given of the breadth of application of this technique which can serve, on the one hand, the needs of scholars studying our natural environment and the many different aspects of man's social and historical development, and on the other, practical and ever-growing problems of wise exploitation of the earth's resources, and of use of the living-space available to mankind.

Photographic interpreters are concerned with the whole range of natural and artificial features visible on the earth's surface, their extent and inter-relationships, and the exact position of the features must be known in order that the fullest information may be gained. For this reason, the use of air photographs for cartography is of fundamental importance. In countries that have long been mapped, the value of detailed surveys is apt to be taken for granted, but in fact the development of air survey as a means of accurate and rapid mapping represents the greatest single advance ever made in the systematic exploration of the earth's crust. Photographs taken under the right conditions will not only yield information for the construction of detailed maps, as Mr Williams explains in Chapter II, but they may be studied themselves either singly or, better still, as overlapping pairs, when use of a stereoscope enables the eye to appreciate the surface relief and so gain a three-dimensional picture. Moreover, a photograph, in contrast to a map, makes no selection of the features that are recorded, and so conveys far more detail of a landscape, and correspondingly richer material for interpretation than a map can ever do (Plate 1). The possibility of establishing from air photographs the relief of a surface, and of expressing this in terms of contours, means that maps so constructed may present all the essential information furnished by survey on the ground. Air survey conducted under carefully controlled conditions both as to flying and as to photography is in fact capable of yielding far more information about the dimension of height than is commonly presented on any maps. British Ordnance Survey maps at 1 : 63,360 scale customarily show contours at 50-feet intervals, and of these, only the contours at intervals of 100 feet, up to 1000 feet in altitude, and thereafter at every multiple of 250 feet, were actually measured on the surface. Accurate air survey, now regularly in use, permits contours to be drawn at intervals of 10 feet or less, in a fraction of the time taken by surveyors on the ground. The possibility of establishing contours at really close intervals means that expression may be given to many small but important details of physical geography and geology, which at present hardly appear on maps at all. The method, too, has important commercial applications involving the assessment of volume, exemplified by the accurate measurement of the potential water storage capacity of a valley, of the content (bulk) of large dumps of fuel, or of the volume of rock to be excavated for the construction of motor-ways or other major engineering works.

To the geologist air photography offers the opportunity for regional surveys to assess geological structure and mineral resources far more quickly than by painstaking survey on the ground. The technique makes possible rapid advances in our knowledge of the geological structure of the earth's crust, that could not otherwise be contemplated because of the labour involved. In this respect it must be emphasised that air survey cannot entirely replace ground reconnaissance: much detailed work will still have to be done on the surface by trained investigators, since the most valuable results will come from the closest integration of work conducted both from the air and on the ground. Here we see the proper function of air photography: by undertaking a comprehensive survey, attention can be drawn to those features of special significance which call for detailed study. By such careful analysis and selection, air reconnaissance can effect, as Dr Hey shows in Chapter III, an immense saving of time for trained scientists working in the field, while in unmapped, or ill-mapped, country the photographs can be of great assistance to a surveyor serving as a base-map for positioning himself on the ground.

Plate 3. The Church Stretton valley, Shropshire, looking south-west (foreground at SJ513018). The valley is determined by one of the important fault-lines in the geology of Britain. To right is the upland plateau of the Longmynd: to left, the prominent hills of the Lawley, Caer Caradoc and Ragleth Hill form the valley side, while to left again lie the successive escarpments of Hoar Edge, of Wenlock Edge and of the Aymestry Limestone.
Y 85

27 July 1947

Plate 3. Church Stretton valley

The quantity of geological information to be gained depends upon the nature of the surface, the variety and complexity of the geology, the extent of exposures and the degree to which the presence of different rocks may be reflected by variations in vegetation overlying them. In Britain, as in much of lowland Europe, the covering of surface-soil and the highly artificial nature of the landscape inevitably limits the application of the method, but if the scene be transferred to the young mountain ranges of the Middle East, we see how clearly major structural features may be visible, free of a covering of soil. The air photographs upon which a structural geologist has to work do not usually yield up their information so easily. The geology has often to be interpreted from careful study of the surface, seen in relief when air photographs are viewed in a stereoscope, and taking account of responses of vegetation to changes in the soil, which in turn reflect differences in the rocks beneath.

Reference has already been made to the covering of soil and rock-waste, or 'drift', to use the geological term, that frequently overlies and masks outcrops of solid rock. The formation of soils, variously derived from the weathering of rocks, involves many different processes by no means all fully understood. This is a subject of fundamental importance in many different studies, for soils reflect recent geological and climatic history, and for this reason they have particular interest for Quaternary research, which is concerned with the changing conditions of environment in the very recent geological past.

Soils may assume, or may have impressed upon them, structures or shapes characteristic of the conditions under which they accumulated. Examples are desert sand-dunes, gravels and screes, and the multiplicity of glacial deposits of special interest in those regions of the earth recently covered by ice. The glacial deposits found in parts of Scotland, and widespread in Ireland (Plate 4), are so remarkably 'fresh', and unmodified by human agency, that they constitute most important material for study and interpretation. Air photography has much to contribute to these studies, for the detailed topography of glacial deposits hardly finds expression on maps of whatever scale, since the contours are drawn at too wide intervals to reveal such small differences of relief. The forms of glacial deposits can be effectively illustrated in both oblique and vertical photographs, which may define their interrelationships, not always apparent on the ground. In arable land, differences in colour of soil reveal the former existence of lakes and pools long vanished. This study has much more than academic interest, for such soils may, by analysis of their contained pollen, yield important

evidence for dating not only themselves, but geological deposits associated with them, so enabling the detailed succession of events in the Quaternary period to be established. Many aspects of glaciation of districts from which ice has now receded (Plate 2), may most profitably be compared with photographs of regions still glaciated at the present day. Indeed, air photography offers the only practical means for detailed survey of the glacier-systems of great mountain ranges, and of the interesting marginal areas of the polar ice-caps, difficult though the flying conditions may be.

Besides its value for survey and research air photography is an important medium for exposition and teaching. Plate 3, a panoramic view looking south-west along the Church Stretton valley of Shropshire, displays this area of complicated geological structure in a fashion that cannot easily be appreciated from any point on the ground. The two sides of the valley are defined by important fault-lines, the floor having been dropped down between rigid blocks of older rocks. On the right is the flat-topped plateau of the Longmynd, composed of a great thickness of sedimentary rocks of Precambrian age. On the left three prominent hills define the valley side; the nearest is the triangular peak of the The Lawley, with the higher Caer Caradoc behind, partly hiding the rounded mass of Ragleth Hill, with Hope Bowdler to the left again, all comprising very ancient volcanic rocks. Apart from these hills, the country there is composed of sandstones, shales, and limestones of various geological formations of Lower Palaeozoic age. The outcrops of the hard rocks form escarpments; first comes the curving line of Hoar Edge, with the thin line of Wenlock Edge in the distance, and the parallel escarpment of the Aymestry Limestone beyond. Thus the essential geological features of the landscape emerge clearly enough, and in great contrast to the man-made agricultural patterns, influenced though these are by the geology. The small mosaic of hedged fields is confined to the flat ground and the lower slopes, the higher ground affording at best rough grass pasture interspersed with bracken. It is interesting, too, to see that the most striking single planned feature of the landscape is a Roman road, still visible after centuries of land use, its line running in a purposeful course down the centre of the valley, the easiest natural

---

Plate 4. Partly submerged drumlins, Clew Bay, Mayo, Eire, looking east. A sector of the archipelago of drumlins in Clew Bay. On the exposed west side of the outer drumlins (foreground) small cliffs have been formed by wave attack. Elsewhere sand and shingle spits are developing.
AJU 94   *11 July 1964*

Plate 4. Partly submerged drumlins

route to the upper Teme, the Aymestry gap and the Herefordshire plain. The emphasis in the analysis of this particular photograph happens to be on structural geology, but other photographs could be chosen to illustrate a great variety of topics in physical geology with gain both to the student in his understanding of such features and to the teacher in his teaching.

Air photography may also be employed to record geographical and geological changes in progress at the present day (Plates 5-6). These are of considerable variety, including soil-creep, the flooding of valleys, silting of estuaries, erosion of coasts, formation of sand-spits, shifting of sand-dunes, besides effects for which opportunity to record comes seldom, like the growth and development of volcanic cones. Valley flooding, of special importance in connexion with agricultural use of land, and the accretion of silt in salt-marshes and estuaries, are not only topics of interest to geologists, but matters of immediate practical concern. Studies of silt-accumulation and growth of salt-marsh, to which Professor Steers refers in Chapter IV, have been in progress for many years, for example, at Scolt Head Island on the north Norfolk coast. There is no way as effective as air photography for recording annual changes in intricate patterns of creeks and saltings, which have to be measured and understood before the principles determining the accumulation of silt along a shore-line can be established. In England land-reclamation round the coast-line of the Lincolnshire fens is a live issue, but land-shortage may some day focus attention, great though the engineering problems be, on the much larger scheme of enclosing the whole of the Wash to gain 200 square miles of land, not to mention capacity for fresh-water storage in addition. The growth of sand-spits and bars, and the progress of coastal erosion are further topics that lend themselves particularly well to study by air photographs. Here the value of photographs in repeated series at known intervals is evident, and the information so gained grows out of all proportion when the results of successive surveys are combined. Major changes round our coasts occur seldom; the most striking example in modern times being the coastal flooding following the North Sea tidal surge in January 1953. But for prompt measures to restore the coast-line this would have effected the greatest change in the geography of East Anglia for several centuries. The recording of rock exposures on inaccessible or remote cliffs can be effectively achieved by low-level oblique photography of the cliff-face, a method that has proved its worth when applied to the Norfolk coast, providing records at known dates of the constantly changing exposures of boulder clay in this important geological section (Plate 6).

For those concerned with physical geography and geology, air photographs offer great advantages in that they record the state of the earth's surface with a wealth of detail not ordinarily presented on maps, however large the scale. Systematic photography of land forms (Plates 1-4) is of the highest importance for the understanding of geographical and physiographical processes. The seepage of springs, the erosion of streams, the incising of rivers, the formation of alluvial plains, the development of slopes, the study of land-slips and of soil-creep, are all important aspects of the evolution of landscape. When studied regionally they have much to reveal about the history of rivers, particularly in relation to the recent changes in sea-level known to have occurred in many parts of the world. Coastal dunes, and the light soils of wind-blown, sandy heaths, like the Breckland of Suffolk, or the 'warrens' of north Lincolnshire, provide the environment often chosen for habitation by prehistoric man, while other evidence of human occupation in these early periods is to be found in sand-deposits and caves, marking 'raised beaches'—the term used to describe old strand-lines formed when the sea stood at a higher level than now. Towards the end of the prehistoric period, when man began to develop an agricultural economy, the growth of crops first came to be practised on such fertile soils as the loess of south-east Europe, or the gravels and silts of river-valleys, enriched by periodic flooding. Air photographs of these features are thus of value not only as a contribution to our understanding of the geographical processes involved but as a guide to sites of early human occupation. Such studies are important, particularly in comparison with photographs of similar areas where vegetation still exists in its natural state, for they enable us to reconstruct the geographical and physical environment in which mankind developed in the long twilight of prehistory. This is a subject in which the techniques of geology, geography, botany and archaeology all merge, with great profit to each as studies in Quaternary research have shown.

Plate 5. Soil-creep, Cotswold escarpment, near Brockworth, Gloucestershire (SO898148). In southern England many steep hill-slopes, particularly those composed of sands and clays of Mesozoic age, are unstable, so that the rocks near the surface tend to creep downhill in a series of almost imperceptible slides and flows. Where long continuance of the process causes a belt of broken ground, this is readily recorded on an air photograph but not always so easily appreciated on the surface. In this instance the soil-flows are seen to over-ride medieval fields in ridge and furrow.
PN 21   *13 April 1955*

Plate 5.   Soil-creep

The employment of air photography for surveys of vegetation is well established, and as a means of mapping rapidly major vegetational zones the method has no equal. Much of the world's mantle of vegetation has been interfered with or destroyed by human agency, and it would be of great scientific interest to record on air photographs the distribution of the main plant-communities in the few remaining continental areas where very extensive tracts of 'natural' vegetation, jungle, forest, swamp and prairie, still survive. The information to be gained will depend much upon the scale at which photography is undertaken: coverage at a small scale would be needed to record main vegetation-zones, while photography of selected areas at a large scale (Plate 7) could yield for the ecologist, as Professor Pigott shows in Chapter VI, abundant information of a kind not generally available, since time-consuming surveys on the ground are involved. In Britain, where little vegetation now survives free of human interference, all the more importance attaches to Nature Reserves and comparable areas, where the method has been applied in connexion with special botanical and ecological studies currently in progress. For such work the air photograph is indispensable: there is no other method of recording in detail vegetation in salt-marshes, peat-bogs, rocky shores, cliffs or inaccessible islands. The information to be gained depends much upon the conditions of photography, upon the season at which it is undertaken, and upon local circumstances. To obtain full value from the method as applied to biological problems, photography of the same area should be repeated at intervals to reveal changes in vegetation. Such repetition and continuity of recording is invaluable in planning the management of Nature Reserves for scientific study.

The appearance of deciduous woodland varies much with the season of the year. Photography in winter may penetrate to the ground beneath the tree canopy, enabling the extent of undergrowth and scrub to be assessed, while photography in spring, when trees are coming into leaf, offers the best conditions for identifying different varieties. Here, colour photography comes into its own as a means of distinguishing the different tints and hues of vegetation. Photography has often been used to measure the cubic content of useful timber in standing woodlands, and the scientific management of vegetation offers scope for the air observer in the detection of plant diseases.

The use of air photography for making a census of animal species and for the study of wild animals in their natural habitat is described by Dr Darling in Chapter VIII, while Mr Watson considers in Chapter IX some of the special opportunities for research afforded by problems of game-management in a large African reserve. When very big herds are in question accurate estimates of numbers even by an observer in the air are difficult to make. Air photographs can 'cover' with great rapidity herds that may extend over miles of country so enabling an exact count to be made, while photographs at a large scale convey much information about the composition of a herd by age and sex. Above all, the relations of wild animals to their natural environment is a subject that can be strikingly illustrated by air photographs. The pattern of big herds of migrating ungulates, the inter-relations of different species of wild animals, and their individual grazing habits, can be more effectively illustrated in air photographs than in any other way. Moreover, time presses; the next generation may witness the virtual extinction of unprotected herds of large land animals. All the more importance, therefore, attaches to opportunities now afforded by air photography, in Africa and elsewhere, for the study of animal communities in their natural habitat, and their effects on vegetation.

Other species can be studied by the same means; for example, seals and caribou in sub-arctic regions have been the subjects of aerial counts (Plates 45-6). In Britain, opportunities for such work are much restricted as no large wild animals remain. However, air photography here has been applied successfully to counting birds, using both vertical and oblique photography. The gulleries on the Ravenglass sand-dunes, in Cumberland, and the oyster-catcher roosts round Morecambe Bay, in Lancashire, where the birds are serious predators on the local shell-fish beds, have been treated in this way (Plate 47). As instances of the fine detail that can be recorded from the air, mention may be made of changes in the reed beds in some Norfolk Broads owing to activities of the coypu, or to vegetational changes in the South Downs and elsewhere, caused by the near-extinction of the rabbit population by myxomatosis.

The question of the application of air photography to the location of shoals of pelagic fish, and the distribution of the organisms on which they feed, remains uninvestigated upon a large scale. Given suitable photographic technique it might be possible to distinguish the various

---

Plate 6.   Erosion of cliffs, Norfolk coast, near Trimingham (TG285387). A striking illustration of the rapid erosion taking place on these cliffs, composed of boulder clay overlying stratified sediments. Photography, repeated at intervals, is the only practicable means of recording the constantly changing exposures in the 15 miles of cliffs that comprise this important geological section.
WK 27

5 June 1958

Plate 6. Erosion of cliffs

bodies of water—Baltic, Arctic and Atlantic—in the North Sea. The circulation and mixing of these waters, of importance to oceanographers, is a factor determining the movement of fish. In the interest of international economy, and for conservation and the wise use of this form of food, this matter is manifestly worth attention.

Any account of the contribution that air photography can make to development and research in agriculture must involve some cross-reference to disciplines already mentioned. Possibly its greatest use is for soil surveys, such as Dr Perrin describes in Chapter V, which have been undertaken on a wide scale in many parts of the world. In countries with rapidly developing agriculture, regional surveys are indispensable for planning the best use of land and assessing its suitability for any given crop. The results are of value not only for agriculture, but for the scientific study of the history of soils and of the rocks from which they are derived. In Britain, where ice-action in recent geological time has greatly modified the land, soils over large areas are formed from glacial deposits, so that soil-mapping assumes additional importance as it may reveal the extent of different boulder clays, and thus of their parent ice-sheets. Soil erosion occurring in many parts of the world may be surveyed from the air to yield information of great practical value in planning preventive measures or in combating the effects of this menace.

In countries with long-established agriculture increases in population bring ever-increasing conflict of interests in the use of land. Here air photography becomes important in planning the most effective agricultural use of 'marginal land', that is land not already intensively exploited for agriculture. Britain has a highly developed pattern of land use, and such marginal land, of small extent only in the lowland zone, is largely confined there to sandy heaths, peat bogs and marsh; in the highland zone it may comprise the slopes and foot hills of the main ranges, where the tide of agriculture never reached, or reached in the Middle Ages and then receded. This constitutes our sole reserve of land remaining to be fully developed for agriculture, and as population grows the question arises whether economic necessity must not force much of it into production. If it is to be developed to full advantage, manifold problems will arise, including the rationalisation of an apparently haphazard mosaic of small fields, the provision of adequate drainage, and the treatment of sour and infertile soils. When large tracts are involved these measures can be planned most effectively by reference to up-to-date air photographs of the whole area, and such photographs are also a pre-requisite for the study of unproductive moorland and

bogs on our northern hills with a view of their improvement for sheep-grazing.

The use of air photography in connexion with crop-trials and for the assessment of plant disease, leading to treatment and control, is as yet little past the stage of experimentation. Dr Rishbeth discusses in Chapter VII the detection of potato-blight in the Cambridgeshire fens, work in which infra-red film has proved its value. Sugar beet and cereal crops have been the subject of such studies in the United States, with valuable results; this is a field in which colour film, and perhaps the so-called 'false colour' film, responding to differences in the chlorophyll content of the vegetation, may give significantly better results than can be obtained in black and white.

The extent to which air survey can assist the exploration of man's natural environment, as revealed by geology and biology, falls to be considered first amongst the subjects to which air photography can be applied. The study of man's social and cultural development is customarily divided between archaeology and history, both of which gain immeasurably from the application of air photography to their problems. While the two disciplines have essentially the same aim, they differ mainly in the techniques they employ. Archaeology is principally concerned with the long period from the emergence of mankind to the start of literate civilisations in the Greek and Roman world, and includes every concrete manifestation of human activities in its study, while history is essentially dependent on the written word, available in ever-increasing degree from classical times till now, to reveal the interaction of peoples and events. The unity of the two disciplines is well seen in considering the role of air photography which serves both alike. Knowledge is best advanced when the work of scholars in the two subjects can be interwoven and their results combined. Moreover, the value of archaeology as a method of study does not cease with the Roman world; it has much to contribute to all periods down to the present time.

The earliest periods of archaeology are known mainly in terms of implements and artifacts, for no man-made constructions ordinarily survive, certainly none visible from the air. However, from the Neolithic period onwards man has left ever-increasing traces of his existence,

Plate 7. Wytham Woods, Berkshire (SP465087). This vertical photograph taken in diffuse lighting shows the remarkable photographic distinction that can be achieved between different tree species in such mixed deciduous woodland.
V–T 36. Scale 1 : 1,950   *9 June 1961*

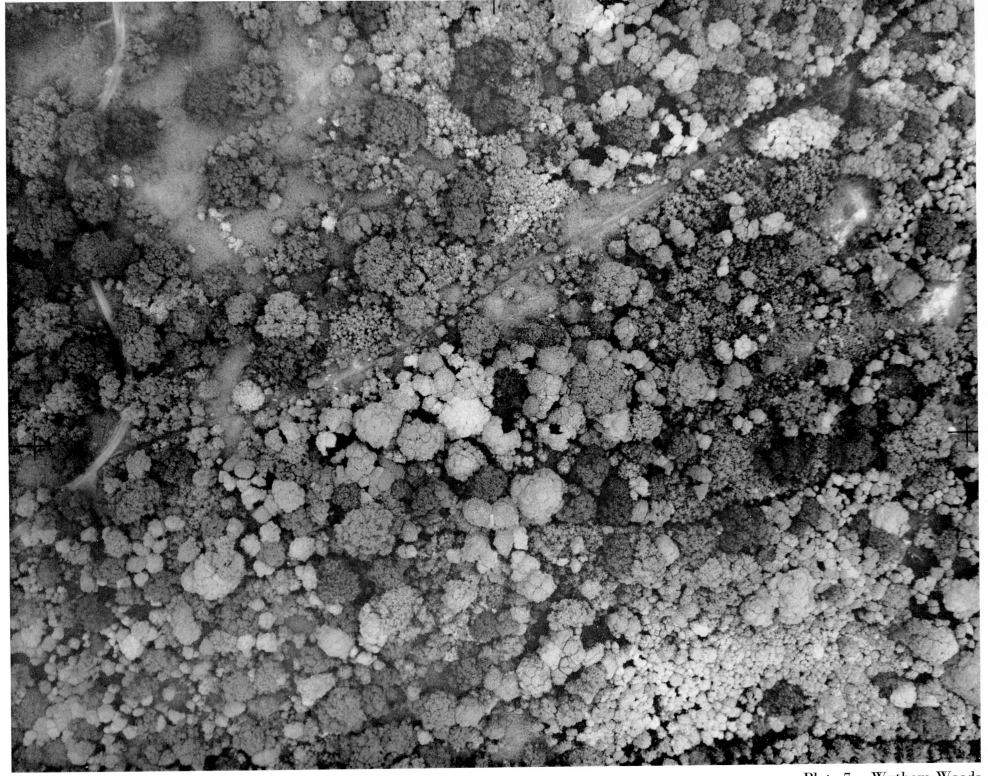

Plate 7. Wytham Woods

and in the last two centuries has exerted such growing mastery over his environment that destruction of ancient and historic sites proceeds apace, as modern 'development' fashions the face of the land anew. Archaeology includes the discovery and examination of all traces of human activities in past ages, principally fortifications, habitations, and agriculture. Much evidence is plain to see, and can be studied on the ground, but in many phases of human development more ancient sites have been levelled or destroyed than the total still visible. Until the advent of air photography, discovery of these buried sites was largely by chance, as when an occasional find revealed the position of an ancient settlement. Today the process of discovery is transformed, since air reconnaissance in competent hands can yield discoveries at a rate previously undreamed-of. Differences in colour and texture of the soil and vegetation revealing buried features are discussed in Chapter X, but many visible constructions in earth or stone, surviving from past ages, may also be examined more rapidly and effectively in terms of air photographs than on the ground. The study of remains of prehistoric peoples can be greatly assisted by surveys of primitive peoples still existing at the present day. Anthropological research in Africa, South America and Asia has much to gain from air photographs of native settlements, tribal customs and agriculture.

Air photography applied to the study of man's environment involves the complete survey of a whole region, or a survey of selected features specified beforehand. In archaeology the case is rather different in that the aim is to discover and to photograph features not previously known to exist. Thus the flying is more in the nature of reconnaissance in which features unknown before may come into the field of view at any time. In this work much depends upon the direction and intensity of the lighting, the length of shadows (Plates 60 and 64), and, when differences in growth and colour of vegetation are in question, the angle of view of the observer in relation to the incidence of sunlight, so that oblique photography comes into its own. Oblique photographs are, moreover, the easiest to take and the most economical of flying time: vertical photographs are still necessary to give an accurate rendering of plan (Plate 58).

When this technique is applied to ancient constructions in North Africa and the Middle East, conditions are found to be somewhat different from those in north-west Europe. The arid climate and absence of vegetation may leave whole cities lying bare, save only for their own ruins and a light covering of sand (Plate 8). Excellent photographs exist, for example, of the desert trading-city of Hatra,[3] in Iraq, surrounded by siege-works, or of Samarra, medieval Baghdad, showing miles of processional avenues, palaces, store-houses, temples and other buildings so clearly that the illustrations would themselves serve as a plan. Apart from deserted Graeco-Roman cities of Greece and Italy, no prizes like this await the archaeological air observer in Europe. Conversely, the subtle variations in vegetation so sensitive to buried features are hardly to be found in the deserts of the Middle East. There, air reconnaissance may bring ancient sites to knowledge by recording their remains, which may have escaped attention hitherto, simply by reason of their remoteness from the beaten track.

This multiplication of discoveries at a rate unmatched before has come at a time of increasing demands upon the use of land. Never till now has the land surface in many European countries been so subject to change by 'development' of all kinds, including new building, new communications, open-cast quarrying, afforestation and more intensive agriculture. Many of these activities cause deep disturbance of the surface, often extending into the sub-soil and thus effectively destroying any archaeological sites that lie there. Ancient monuments that are known can be investigated in advance of destruction, but planning based upon visible features cannot take account of unknown buried remains. Yet it is often the features that have remained unknown, and therefore undisturbed, that are now amongst the most important for study. At a time when land potentially rich in buried sites is being engulfed by development of all kinds, and when the number of sites threatened with destruction far exceeds the number of skilled excavators, it becomes of first importance to have a comprehensive view of this problem. Only so can the limited resources of archaeology be directed where they are most effective, and a delicate choice has to be made of what to salvage and what not. No means other than air photography exists for assessing the archaeological potentialities of an area where there are no visible remains.

Plate 8. Samarra, Iraq. A small part of the medieval city that extends for some 25 miles beside the Tigris, 65 miles NNW. of Baghdad. The city which was established in the ninth century by Caliph Mu'tasim apparently had a life of little more than fifty years. The photograph provides a detailed record of great processional avenues, palaces, barracks and dwellings laid out with astonishing precision; they are now masked by a light covering of sand.
Vertical photograph; scale c. 1 : 2,200   *about 1919*

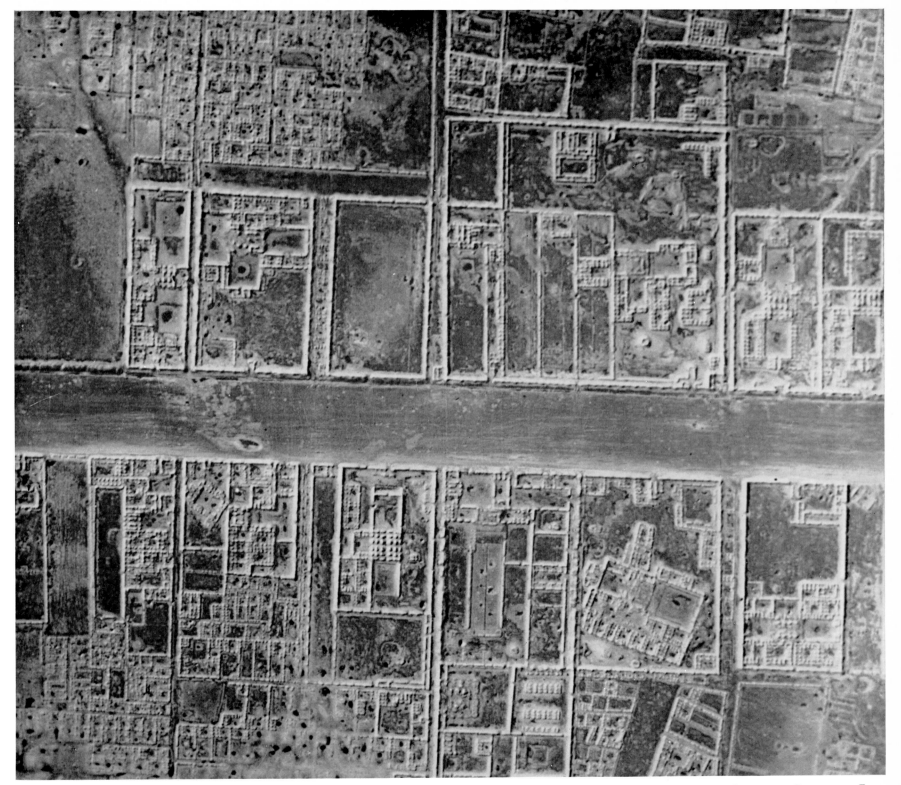

Plate 8.   Samarra, Iraq

As we move to later periods, the material available for study becomes richer and more diverse, and contemporary records immeasurably assist interpretation. For the classical world it may be said that history and archaeology together have established the main framework of events, but in the Roman provinces a great deal of detail has still to be furnished. Air photography has much to contribute: spectacular advances have been made in our knowledge of Roman military organisation in Syria, north Africa and Britain, and the system of land-division and agriculture in Italy and the Mediterranean provinces stands revealed in astonishing detail. Many different facets of life in both the towns and countryside of Roman Britain have been illustrated by this medium of research, and results in other provinces only await the extension of the method.

Amongst the most striking records of Dark Age remains are photographs of sites important in the history of Celtic Christianity in Ireland: Clonmacnois, Inchcleraun and Saint's Island in the Shannon basin, Drumacoo and Devenish, with their extensive earthworks suggesting streets and rows of buildings or cells, and Skellig perched in isolation eight miles out in the Atlantic. In England the revelation of timber buildings of an Anglo-Saxon royal vill, at Yeavering (Plate 61) and at Milfield, both in Northumberland, affords tangible evidence of the life and social conditions described in Beowulf and Bede. Equally far-reaching results are to be expected in mainland Europe if Saxon and Viking sites can be watched and photographed when under vegetation at a sensitive stage of growth.

In the Middle Ages one may view through the medium of air photography the progress of land colonisation and clearance as the tide of settlement moved against the natural forests, the marshes and the moorlands. It was not a steady movement, advance and retreat alternating in response to fluctuations in population and other factors. The thousands of villages that flourished in the early Middle Ages and are now extinct, or are shrunken to a fraction of their former size, testify to economic and agricultural change repeated over many parts of Europe, a reflection of history in which the impact of regional events and local conditions are intertwined. Photographs of medieval towns and villages emphasise the importance to the historian, as Professor Knowles shows in Chapter XI, of studying a ground plan (Plate 9) capable of revealing both the ancient 'fabric' of a village displayed by its street lines, building sites and property boundaries, and also the control imposed on village and urban development by a small number of features, a church, a manor house, a castle, a religious house, even a windmill. Economic history is particularly well served by the evidence that air photographs are almost alone in providing about such activities as agriculture, quarrying, and mining, while it may be observed that all major constructions, whether great castles, town-walls, or the many hundreds of religious houses, express in real terms the wealth and labour of countless thousands of individuals.

Many aspects of modern history are written large upon the face of the land: the development of agriculture and the evolution of communications, with medieval trackways giving place to the turn-pike and the coach-road, and the canals and railways representing the more sophisticated transport of the modern age. We see, too, the changes in social order: by the end of the Middle Ages the building and maintenance of castles was neither necessary nor practical as an expression of an individual's power and prestige, save for the very few. Great country houses, mansions and *châteaux* are the chief remaining visible expression of the wealth and taste of the leading members of the social order of the seventeenth and eighteenth centuries. We hardly realise now the extent to which, in England, these great estates with their fine buildings, often embodying part of the fabric of an existing castle or religious house, their spreading deer parks and landscape gardens, transformed the contemporary countryside. A glance at Saxton's county maps (c. 1575) gives a striking impression of the proportion of the land that came to be emparked in this way. This is a phase of social history that has now almost vanished from the contemporary scene, and with its passing much of beauty has passed too. In England, the avenues of Boughton House, or of Wimpole Hall, in their heyday, or the skilful planning of the Stourhead gardens with their artificial lakes, show the boldness with which landscape could be transformed and beautified. Many aspects of contemporary life in the humble village houses can be effectively

Plate 9. Naarden, which controls the eastern approaches to Amsterdam, is an example of the art of the seventeenth-century military engineer at the climax of its development. The street-plan has its origin in the 'new town' founded about 1350, but the chief interest of Naarden lies in its fortifications, constructed in 1675-85 under the engineer Admiral Dortsman. The medieval town is cramped within defences comprising a huge rampart, from which there project six great spear-head bastions, faced in brickwork: outside this again a double line of water defences forms an exceptionally complicated pattern best appreciated from the air.
R.A.F. photograph 106G 3375 print No. 4067. Scale 1 : 7,550
18 October 1944

Plate 9. Naarden

illustrated by comparing sixteenth- and seventeenth-century plans like those of Norden or Clerke, with air photographs of the same villages today. The church, partly by reason of the solidity of its fabric, is the building most likely to have endured intact; the parsonage, manor-house and windmill, all important in the village life, will ordinarily have suffered some change between complete rebuilding and decay; few sixteenth-century peasant houses, and hardly any that are genuinely medieval, will have survived the successive rebuildings that replaced clay, timber and thatch by the more durable materials, brick and stone. More lasting than the buildings are the earthworks of medieval fields in ridge and furrow, the marl-pits, quarries and fish-ponds, the common lands and marshes, carrying rights of estover and of turbary, all exemplifying important aspects of peasant life seldom described in contemporary records.

Many lands in Europe bear traces of human settlement of different ages; the most distinctive element in the English countryside is the detailed regional variation, a product of the many different cultures brought by successive waves of invaders that anciently swept into these islands, in conjunction with the very varied natural background. The work of numerous generations in developing and moulding the land in which they live is essentially an evolutionary process responding to changing practices and habits. The absence, except for the privileged, of effective means of communication, at least till the eighteenth century, meant that the life of the vast majority of the population was spent in relative isolation in their villages and that everyday needs had perforce to be largely met from local resources. The variety of building-materials, and of building-practice, and the individual architectural styles exhibited by old buildings in our villages, reflect this, while the general pattern of settlement and the village plans, so often displayed in air photographs far better than in a map, illustrate how different communities responded to local conditions.

This wide regional variation and the delicate balance between man and Nature, with villages and fields determined and shaped by the natural environment of landscape and soils, accounts for the living beauty of the English countryside. With such a background modern problems of planning call for considerable knowledge of physical geology and of settlement history if they are to be solved. Here, air photographs are of the utmost value, for they constitute an up-to-date record of the land surface presenting the most varied details of its use. Vertical photographs taken under carefully controlled conditions have all the accuracy of large-scale maps, which may, indeed, be prepared from them. Oblique photographs, which are the easiest for the layman to appreciate, present features partly in plan and partly in elevation, rather in the fashion of an isometric drawing. As applied to individual buildings the quality of comprehension that can be achieved from an elevated view-point was appreciated long ago by such artists as Kip and Loggan.

Problems of regional planning confront many countries of Europe, Britain not least amongst them, by reason of her density of population, her industrial economy, and her shortage of land. Another generation will see the clash between competing interests for the use of land become still more acute. In face of growing demands of land for agriculture, land for housing, land for 'development', for public services and communications, for quarrying, for recreation, and for scientific study, planning that involves piecemeal apportionment of land is not enough. Nothing short of an overall national policy will serve the needs of our crowded islands, and the longer the formulation of such a policy is postponed the greater the ill effects to be reaped. How pressing is the problem may be judged by the fact that each year 50,000-70,000 acres are required to meet the needs of housing,[4] of industry and communications, so that in seven years the countryside will have lost to such use the area of a medium-sized county like Worcestershire.

Air photographs affording an up-to-date record of the surface are widely recognised as indispensable for planning, in view of the complex and overlapping considerations now involved in devising the best use of a highly developed land surface. Maps show selected features only, while in areas of intensive development maps become rapidly out of date. The value of air photographs for planning will be more easily appreciated if some of the issues involved in future planning are briefly mentioned.

Change in land use to meet the needs of building involve a number of important factors, aesthetic and practical. The impairment of amenities of a landscape, and the contraction of open space, are matters upon which a value is not easily set. There can, however, be no doubt about the loss, or the sterilising beneath buildings, of the covering of fertile soil, and the progressive constriction of catchment-areas of unpolluted

Plate 10. Dereliction of industry, east of Merthyr Tydfil, Glamorganshire (SO060070). A vivid impression of the waste land that occurs along the north edge of the South Wales coalfield, with its wilderness of tip-heaps from past phases of coal-mining.
XX 27   *19 April 1959*

Plate 10.　Dereliction of industry

water. These two media, soil and water, are amongst a country's greatest natural assets, and their best use affords a nice exercise in planning. The greatest needs for water, whether for domestic consumption or for industry, by no means coincide with maximum sources of supply, and in future policy both for new towns and for industry these facts fall to be considered.

An age which sees increasing competition for the use of land cannot afford to neglect the wastes that have survived from unplanned industrial development of the last two centuries. The tip-heaps and dereliction remaining from eighteenth- and nineteenth-century coal-mining in South Wales (Plate 10) and in the 'Black Country', the spoil-heaps from the oil-shale industry of the central valley of Scotland, not to mention the scars left by open-cast quarrying for ironstone, clay and gravel in Midland England (Plate 21), need treatment if these areas are to be brought back into effective use. Air photography offers the most rapid means of obtaining an overall view of the problem, as a basis for planning the reconditioning of such land.

Not only are our towns growing in extent, but congested areas within them fall for 'redevelopment', as old buildings reach the end of their useful life, or as space becomes available because of changes in ownership, or for other reasons, not to mention the devastation of war. Replanning within the heart of an old town is a difficult exercise because of the many different and often competing interests involved. Here the air photograph offers great advantages over a ground-plan for it enables the whole of a town to be seen and studied comprehensively when, as Sir Ian Richmond shows in Chapter XII, the importance of individual buildings not only in themselves but in their setting becomes clear. In our old towns, most of the churches and a select company of other buildings are the only genuinely medieval structures to have survived. However, the remarkable persistence of streets, of rights-of-way, property boundaries and lines of town-wall, cause the medieval town-plan, in which is written so much history, to be largely preserved. This is because new building has nearly always proceeded piecemeal: exceptions, as when a town was cleared by fire, are rare. The present age is the first to proceed boldly with wholesale replanning of the centres of old towns, and it remains to be seen whether in modern conditions due attention can be paid not only to economic factors that determine the use and architecture of buildings, or to problems of pedestrian and vehicular access, but also to the long and complicated historical development reflected in a town-plan. Such factors as the high value of urban land, and the strangle-hold of the motor-vehicle, have been slowly changing the face of our towns: gardens are built over, verges and trees are removed, streets are realigned in adjustment to needs of traffic, changes which take place so gradually that their cumulative effect is not easily realised. In respect of traffic congestion air photography has an important contribution to make, for it can provide for the information of planners a visual record at a given time of the state of traffic in a town.

Air photography applied to residential areas has much to show of achievements and failures in planning. It is easy to contrast the gracious terraces and noble architecture of Regency Bath with the poor and over-crowded housing in nineteenth-century industrial towns. Mean and unsuitable dwellings are a reflection of the history and economics of their age. By comparison, modern housing-estates, to which Lord Esher refers in Chapter XIII, have to conform to specified standards of building, and of amenity, laid down by legislation; but what opinion future generations may have of the result the reader may judge from Plate 84. Photographs of dormitory and residential areas of towns can be of considerable assistance to sociological studies. The categorisation of population in such areas by age, or occupation, or income-range, serve the needs of research in certain aspects of economics and sociology, while distance and mode of transport between house and place of work are important practical factors in planning housing-estates and the roads that serve them. Vertical photography at a large scale can provide very quickly a great deal of up-to-date information about the quality, size and type of housing, even to the number of square feet of floor-space, the outbuildings, garages and gardens, so saving the time of research-workers conducting individual enquiry. Such photographs might well be used on an occasion of wholesale revision of rates as a basis for assessment, with the advantage to the Local Authority of saving in time and cost.

Something of the versatility of air photography as an instrument of research will have become apparent from the many uses here described, and the list is by no means exhaustive. Two general fields of application may be emphasised: regional mapping of the earth's surface with a view to the exploitation of natural resources like oil, minerals, timber and water-power, and detailed planning of land use. Consideration of the first field is the theme of several of the following chapters; the importance of the second is by no means generally realised because of the very rate at which man is changing his environment. In all over-crowded countries planning should be exercised on the broadest lines embracing every facet of land use. If the present yearly increasing rate of growth is maintained, the end of this century may see London so linked with neighbouring urban centres that all south-east England may become one vast extent of towns, housing-estates and dormitory suburbs. In the west Midlands, Birmingham-Wolverhampton-Coventry will grow to another such agglomeration, while south Lancashire, Tyneside-Teeside, and Glasgow with its neighbour towns bid fair to be others.

The most careful planning is needed now, if any countryside is to survive at all. The English countryside is Nature, not tamed in green-belts and parks, but seen in wide tracts of farmland, fields and woods, with scattered farms, villages and market towns, so full of history and contributing so much to the beauty of landscape. Here air photography emerges as an instrument that helps to fashion policy. To whose long-term benefit, it may be asked, is the achievement of a specified annual 'growth rate', if the result in another generation is a land with little countryside left? In the meanwhile most careful scrutiny is needed of all projects involving extensive change in the use of land. The establishment of National Parks and Nature Reserves and the preservation of the coastline, all highly desirable within the framework of regional planning, will not be enough to meet the need for open space of a growing population. The fact must be recognised that the countryside is not limitless, and that its unique cultural landscape is irreplaceable.

NOTES

[1] O. G. S. Crawford, 'A Centenary of Air Photography', *Antiquity* **27** (1954), 206, Plate iii.

[2] A full account of the remarkable contribution of air photography to military intelligence in the Second World War has yet to be published. The fine quality of some of the early photographs may be judged from Plate 8, taken nearly fifty years ago.

[3] J. S. P. Bradford, *Ancient Landscapes* (1957), 71-5, Plate xxiv.

[4] Official figures from the Ministry of Housing and Local Government, quoted in *The Countryside in 1970* (H.M.S.O., 1964), 26.

W. W. WILLIAMS

Air Photographs and Cartography

THE cartographer probably more than any other user of air photographs is concerned with their geometry, or with their quantities. The map which he makes must have a known scale which must, within very small limits, be constant. If the scale is not constant its departure from the mean scale must be systematic and known. Altitudes of large numbers of points must be ascertained, and the relief must be shown by means of one of the usual conventions. A map is not respectable if it is not a faithful record of horizontal distances and vertical heights. Thus, while the map-maker must be familiar with all the usual skills of interpretation, his major preoccupation is with techniques which will enable him to make maps which are accurate records of the shape and size of the ground which it represents.

A Cambridge pioneer in mapping from air photographs was H. Hamshaw Thomas[1] who, during the military campaign in Palestine in 1917-18, carried out a survey of 2,000 square miles of inaccessible country with the crude material resources of a non-professional Army Captain of that time. The problems which he then encountered created in Thomas an interest in air photography which he never lost. He was engaged in photographic interpretation during the war of 1939-45 as a Squadron Leader in the Royal Air Force, and from 1950 to 1956 was Chairman of the Cambridge Committee for Aerial Photography.

Thomas was the inspirer of the work done in Cambridge between 1920 and 1923 by Griffiths[2] and Jones.[3] This is described in *Aerial Surveying by Rapid Methods*.[4] It was a tragedy that Griffiths was killed in a flying accident in October 1923. But for this the progress of research in aerial surveying in Cambridge might have been a continuous story; but when he died research in Cambridge, and indeed in the whole country, received a check from which it never recovered.

The pioneers were not mistaken in their advocacy of mapping from air photographs. Ground surveying involves innumerable detailed observations which in favourable terrain are slow and expensive, and in difficult country, such as mountains and marshes, often become almost impossible. By contrast an aircraft is capable of photographing hundreds of square miles in an hour. To an aircraft no country is inaccessible, and problems of disease, often a great danger to surveyors, do not exist.

Plate 11 shows marshes in Norfolk which are difficult to negotiate on foot, and which are covered at high tide. To survey the detail shown on the photograph would probably take a plane-tabler a week. From photographs the detail could be plotted to any reasonable degree of accuracy in two hours.

Economically air surveys have the very great advantage that the finished map can, therefore, be produced in a relatively short time, a matter of great importance to those who are interested in agricultural or industrial development. In the past to survey 1,000 square miles needed the recruitment and the employment of a large staff for something like two years. Nowadays an aircraft might take the photographs in a day, and the largest process in the whole operation would be the provision of the necessary ground control; but recent advances in techniques have made it possible to do even this quite rapidly.

Other contributors to this volume discuss the varied problems of interpreting air photographs. The surveyor encounters the same problems except that he must interpret the *whole* of the ground. A map with blank spaces is no map. Thus when, on air photographs, clouds or trees obscure the terrain the surveyor is denied the means of doing his job. The most favourable conditions possible are necessary for survey photography; a clear atmosphere, no clouds, and a minimum of wind and turbulence. *All* of the ground must be covered by strips of photographs taken, ideally, from the same height, with a uniform fore and aft overlap of 60 per cent; the reason for this overlap will be given later. The side overlap between strips, known as the lateral overlap, creates especial difficulties. Theoretically it may be very small. But when a pilot attempts to steer a course giving a very small overlap, a slight variation from his course may result in there being no overlap at all. These gaps cause great embarrassment to the surveyor, for not only do they mean blank spaces on the map, but, the size of the blanks being unknown, the relative positions of areas on either side cannot be determined.

The great contribution which the aircraft offers to the surveyor is a new platform for his instruments; and it is profitable to consider the advantages and complexities involved in the use of this platform in any consideration of the value of photogrammetry[5] as a survey method. Before the aircraft, the methods of the surveyor could be reduced to a number of linear and angular measurements made at ground level. These measurements might be of extreme accuracy, but they bore little obvious relation to the form of the resultant map. Base lines, triangulation processes, lines of levels, all of these needed a great deal of treatment, compilation and development, followed by the detailed field processes of plane-tabling or chain-surveying, before any semblance of the map appeared. By contrast, the aerial camera at once produces something very near to a map. When pointed vertically downwards the camera produces in one rapid operation a pictorial representation of the ground in which fields, houses, roads, rivers and all else appear in their true juxtapositions. One could, with the help of such a photograph, decide how most conveniently to walk from one place to another; the shapes of fields and delineations of roads and rivers are apparent. That is to say, the first field observation appears to be very like a map. What we have to do is to find out how far this photograph compares with the conventional kind of map in accuracy and in general usefulness.

Some obvious difficulties at once present themselves. First, the ground surveyor, when he sets up his instrument, carefully centres it over a known point of observation, and then levels it. Probably, too, he knows the height of the observation station, so that when he measures the height of his instrument axis, or telescope, above this point, he knows precisely where his instrument is placed. Another way of expressing this is to say that he knows the co-ordinates of his instrument in X and Y, or in latitude and longitude, and in Z, or altitude. Now the camera in the aircraft is being transported at high speed through a mobile atmosphere, so that its position at the instant of observation in X, Y and Z cannot be 'pre-arranged'; indeed this is difficult to determine *after* the instant of exposure or observation. Moreover, the camera cannot be orientated or levelled as can the theodolite, and there will almost certainly be unknowns in tilts and orientations. These may be considered as rotations about three axes, namely the line of flight, a

horizontal line perpendicular to the line of flight and the vertical; they are generally referred to as ω, ϕ and κ rotations.

We see then that our new instrument, the aerial camera, while it has the advantage of a unique point of view, suffers from possible movement in all the six 'degrees of freedom' detailed above, and some of the complications arising from this instability of the camera must be simply described. Indeed, in this short account of the process of mapping from air photographs it is helpful to start with the ideal case of a truly vertical photograph of flat ground, which provides something like a map, and then to consider the difficulties and limitations that arise, and the means of dealing with them.

In Fig. 1, L represents the camera lens, ab the plane of the film or plate in the camera—the focal plane—and AB the ground. Thus the photographic image ab represents a ground length AB. The scale of the photograph is therefore $ab/AB = f/H$, where f is the focal length of the camera lens, and H the height of the camera above the ground. This simple statement ignores minor considerations such as lens distortion, which for convenience are omitted from this discussion, but which are important in the whole story.

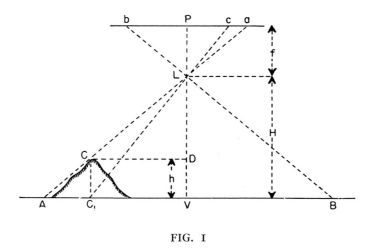

FIG. I

Now in Fig. 1, suppose that one half of the ground photographed is h feet higher than AB. In the corresponding half of the photograph the scale would then be $aP/CD = f/H-h$. Thus, if there are variations in the height of the terrain shown in a picture, there will be variations in the picture scale. This effect is obvious to any photographer; features

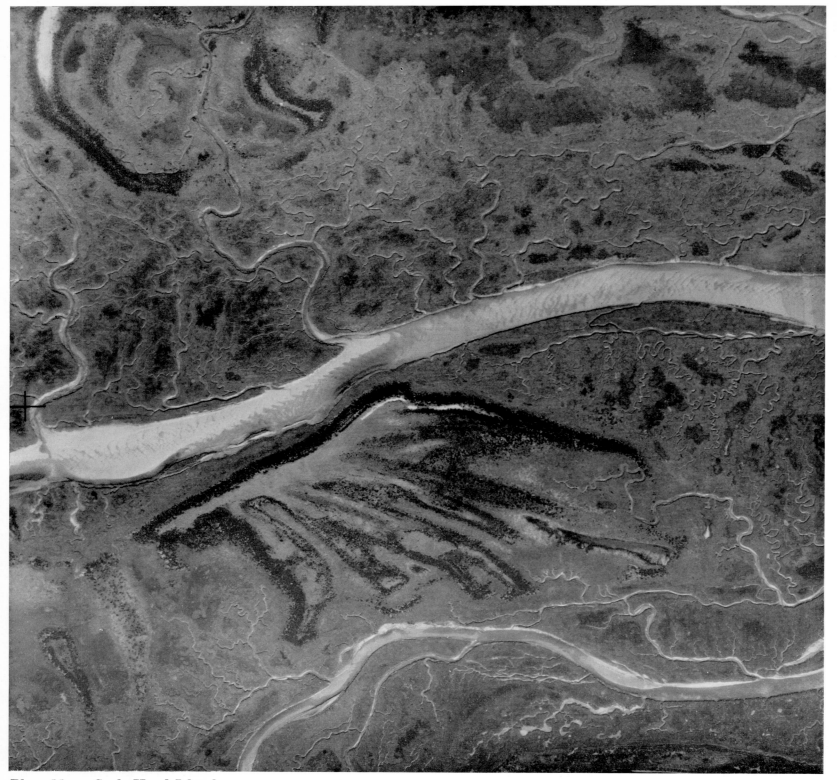

Plate 11a.   Scolt Head Island

Plates 11a and b. Scolt Head Island, Norfolk (TE820460). Stereo-pair of vertical photographs; Williamson F.24 camera, f = 8″. The photographs show the intricate pattern of sand and shingle ridges, creeks and salterns characteristic of this sector of coastline. V–AT 63–64. Scale 1 : 3,650
5 June 1962

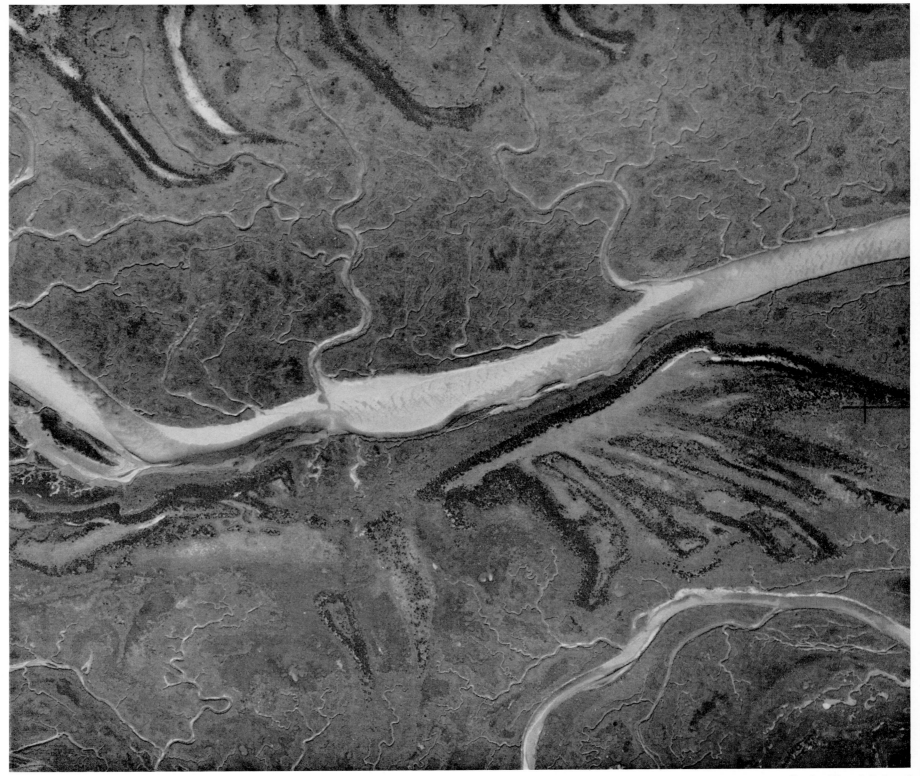

Plate 11b. Scolt Head Island

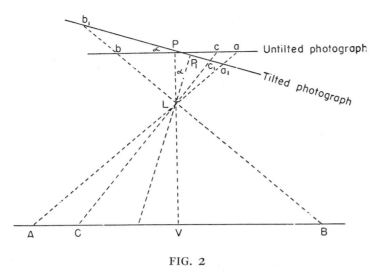

FIG. 2

nearest to the camera appear largest. The grotesquely disproportionate size of the feet of a person photographed sitting in a deckchair is a homely example of what this distortion means. As an example of the magnitude of the scale-change due to variation in the height of the ground, a photograph taken with a camera $f = 1$ foot from a height 10,000 feet above M.S.L. would have a scale of 1/10,000. But if ground were included whose height was 1,000 feet above M.S.L.—which could well happen in this country—the scale would be 1/9,000; a quite appreciable variation and one that would not be tolerated in a survey made by ground methods. Along with the distortion in scale, linear displacement occurs, and this is equally unacceptable. For instance, in Fig. 1, the top of a mountain C forms an image at a; but the vertical projection of C to C' in the datum plane AB would form an image at c. This linear displacement ac is known as 'height distortion'; it can be of considerable magnitude on the edges of photographs. Clearly there will be no such distortion at the plumb-point V.

Camera tilts create equally embarrassing distortions. The geometry of tilt distortions is not difficult to understand: but it is difficult in practice to determine how great the tilts are. In Fig. 2, suppose the camera axis to be tilted at an angle α with the vertical; P_i is now the principal point of the photograph, so that the distances of the images A, B and C from this new principal point are $P_i a_i$, $P_i b_i$, and $P_i c_i$, which can be seen in the diagram to differ considerably from Pa, Pb, and Pc in the

untilted photograph. It is also apparent that the scale of the photograph at a_i will be greater than that at b_i.

These brief accounts of height and tilt distortion are sufficient to demonstrate that, quantitatively, the air photograph is likely to fall far short of the standards required by the ordinary map user. Distances and areas measured on a photograph may be very misleading, and it is necessary to devise methods of plotting from the photographs so that these distortions are eliminated in the resultant map.

But, before discussing how to compile the map, another deficiency in the single photograph must be considered; the photograph, being recorded in one plane, is a two-dimensional record which is obviously incapable of providing any mathematical evidence of the third dimension of ground height. It is true that our interpretation of the picture may provide some clue as to the relief. Obviously rivers will run through the valley bottoms; pinnacle peaks are likely to be identifiable, and shadows may give some clue to slopes. But heights cannot be measured; the information simply is not there. But the situation is greatly changed if we use two photographs taken from different view points. In Fig. 3, TF is a feature—a mountain, a chimney, or a house—of which T is the top and F the foot. Photographs are taken at two air stations first at L_i and then at L_{ii}. The distance between them is the air base B; that is to say, the ground distance travelled by the aircraft between exposures. Images of T and F are formed at t_i and f_i on the first photograph and at t_{ii} and f_{ii} on the second: $(P_i f_i + P_{ii} f_{ii}) = p$ is called the *parallax* of the ground point F, and it can be seen that a simple relationship $p/f = B/H$

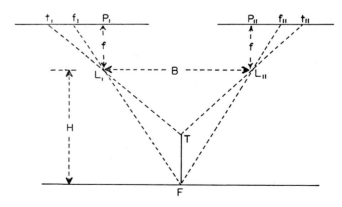

FIG. 3

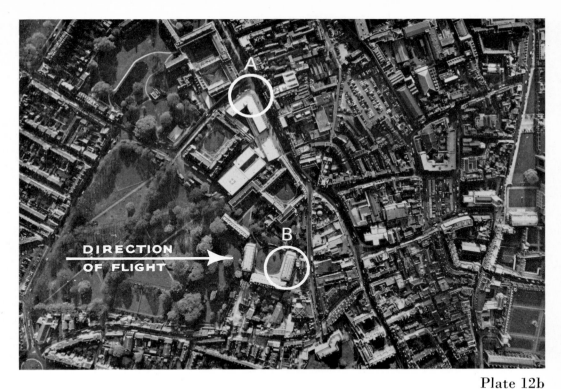

Plate 12a

Plate 12b

Plate 12a and b. Cambridge (TL452583). Stereo-pair of vertical photographs; Fairchild K.17 camera, f = 6".
K.17, Misc. 59–60.   Scale 1 : 4,700   30 October 1962

exists. This is known as the parallax equation. From it H can be determined if p, f and B are known. The equation in this form is not convenient to use; but when differentiated to give

$$dp = -\frac{fB}{H^2}\,dH$$

it is a simple matter to ascertain how much higher a given point is above another. In Fig. 3 it can be seen that the higher point T has a parallax $(P_t t_\prime + P_{\prime\prime} t_{\prime\prime})$ which is greater than that of the lower point $F = (P_\prime f_\prime + P_{\prime\prime} f_{\prime\prime})$; that is to say an increase of parallax indicates an increase in altitude. The simplest method of measuring height differences is to measure parallax differences with an instrument known as a parallax bar. This is a simple micrometer measuring device designed for use in conjunction with a stereoscope. More elaborate machines for height determination must inevitably measure parallax directly or indirectly.

On the complicated machines which are now much in favour the parallax measurement is linked to other settings for f, B and H, and heights can be measured.

Parallactic displacement can be seen very clearly on the overlapping pair of photographs (Plate 12). The relative positions of the tops and bottoms of the buildings ringed in white and marked A and B, are clear evidence of the heights of the buildings. It is this apparent displacement which permits an accurate determination of the dimension of height.

The profession of photogrammetry, then, consists primarily of solving the three problems of height distortion, tilt distortion and height determination. Of height determination little more will be said than that the parallax formula given above must be used with caution. Refinements are necessary in order to obviate errors in height which might be introduced by the accidents of tilt, or by lens distortion. Instruments must be so designed as to give a high rate of output. An additional complication recently encountered was that the field of view of the camera was so wide, and the aircraft flown so high, that even on a single photograph the curvature of the earth caused appreciable error, for which corrections had to be applied.

Early attempts at solving the general problem of mapping from air photographs resorted to three-dimensional geometry. It would be possible, if the co-ordinates of sufficient ground points appearing on the photographs were known, to resect the position of the air camera in space. It would then be possible, from a succession of such air stations, to fix the positions of unknown ground points in three dimensions by intersection, in a way comparable to that of intersecting points in two dimensions with the plane table. Thus the detail of the map could be completed in three dimensions. But such a process would be very slow and laborious, and it was early realised by the pioneers that economy demanded some more expeditious means of solving the problem.

A second method exploited the fact that, subject to certain corrections due to tilt, a photograph is angle-true at its centre. That is to say that within the limits of accuracy of measurement the angles subtended at the centre by other points on the photograph are the same as those between corresponding points on the ground. This is an important property, and for many years useful work has done with the help of comparatively simple, but very accurate, co-ordinate-measuring machines known as stereo-comparators. The method lost favour for high precision work because of the very cumbersome computations involved, but there is now evidence that modern computing methods may restore it to favour. For less accurate work simple graphical methods and some ingenious devices such as the slotted template apparatus have been used extensively to good effect.

Probably the most elegant method of resolving the problem is by means of the modern stereo-plotting machine. Such instruments are complex; they vary in detail but their principles are the same. All of them attempt to restore in miniature the conditions obtaining at the time of photography for successive pairs of photographs. The photographs are set up at a distance apart which is a known fraction (the scale) of the real distance. They are viewed stereoscopically, and are then manipulated so that the relative tilts between the two photographs are faithfully restored, or re-set. This is possible from the evidence of the photographs alone, and the process can be reduced to a rule-of-thumb routine. At this stage we have a picture in relief, or *model* as it is called, which can be examined, measured in three dimensions, enlarged or reduced in size, and rotated by manipulation of the instrument

movements. The model at this stage, is the result of restoring the planes of the photographs relative to one another, but so far no effort has been made to restore these planes to their true positions with reference to the ground. This is done by final adjustments, for which it is obvious that some ground control, or known ground points are required (a minimum of three to define a plane). The model can then be enlarged or reduced in order to bring it to the correct scale, and rotated in order to make it fit the datum plane. The scale adjustment is made by increasing or decreasing the length of the instrument base, and the model is tilted by ω and ϕ rotations which tilt the whole model until the 'model' heights agree with the known ground heights. Instrument designers and manufacturers have produced instruments which make it possible to do all this rapidly, and with ease. Once the setting is made, the operator has merely to steer his indicator mark along the detail, or along contour lines, and the map is drawn. A recent trend in instrument development is to elaborate these instruments so that co-ordinates may be read at once; they may even be printed. Scanning devices, which may eliminate human errors, and at the same time increase the rate of output have been suggested. In a variety of ways instruments are changing rapidly, but the changes are elaborations rather than introductions of new principles.

The accuracy of maps so produced can be high, and some remarkable claims have been made for the precision of modern instruments. It is normally expected that plan work should be accurate to 0·1 mm. on the scale of the photograph; and, as there are reasons for photographing at scales near the scale of the resultant map, this represents a very satisfactory degree of accuracy. Heights should be accurate to within at least 1/5,000 of the flying height. That is to say, if the aircraft were flying at 10,000 feet, heights on the map should be accurate to within 2 feet more or less. These are average statements of the degree of precision to be expected; in favourable circumstances better results have been obtained.

In general, mapping by air photographs has passed all the tests of accuracy for all ordinary purposes. Any shortcomings that it may have are, not surprisingly, the result of the remoteness of the camera from the ground. Gaps may occur because of shadows caused by clouds or by buildings. Trees can create obvious difficulties. 'Dead ground', screened from the view of the camera, occurs for instance in narrow streets on the edge of a photograph. This difficulty is particularly embarrassing in mapping on large scales where the omission of small, but important details cannot be tolerated. Another very real difficulty is that few machine operators today have had any experience as field surveyors, and so do not readily appreciate or interpret all that is in a photograph. Recent tests have shown that some maps made from air photographs have been seriously incomplete for this reason. To interpret the whole of a photograph is, of course, extremely difficult. One example will suffice to explain this. It has not proved possible to classify roads from middle- and small-scale photographs. This may become easier in future as two way roads are constructed; but in general, photographs can be very misleading as to the importance or classification of roads.

Some reference must be made to the technical aids which are frequently suggested, and often eagerly seized upon. Radar is invaluable in its various forms as an aid to navigation and for fixing aircraft positions. Heights, or rather depths below the aircraft, can now be measured by means of a kind of electronic echo-sounder. Statoscopes provide accurate evidence of variations of height in flying; ancillary cameras provide evidence of tilt. At the same time the photographs improve; cameras take clearer pictures, their angle of view becomes wider, while improved film emulsions make it possible to discern detail with increasing refinement.

Nothing has so far been said about the uses of oblique photographs, that is, photographs taken from cameras pointing sideways and downwards from an aeroplane. Such photographs have the advantage of covering much larger areas of ground, but the disadvantage of having varying scales. They have been used for small-scale mapping, but it is evident that their usefulness, by comparison with vertical photographs, must be very limited.

The techniques and instruments very briefly described above combine to make a method of map-making which can be applied wherever an aircraft can fly. Impassable marshes, inaccessible mountains, deserts whether hot or frozen, enemy territory, all may now be mapped at leisure once the photographs are taken. Some ground work is still necessary in order that the work should be 'controlled' as to scale and datum plane. It would be almost true to say that, save for the obvious handicap of gaps due to cloud or faulty navigation, the accuracy of the map is now limited by the amount of ground work available rather than by any defect in the photographs or photogrammetric method.

NOTES

[1] The late H. Hamshaw Thomas, M.B.E., F.R.S., Sc.D. Sometime Reader in Plant Morphology.

[2] Major J. C. Griffiths.

[3] Sir B. Melville Jones, A.F.C., F.R.S., Francis Mond Professor of Aeronautical Engineering, 1919-52.

[4] Cambridge, 1925.

[5] Photogrammetry. A clumsy word for which no accepted alternative has been found. It is used for the process of making maps from photographs. Originally it was applied to mapping from ground photographs, but latterly it has been associated entirely with air photographs.

R. W. HEY

Geological Uses of Air Photographs

SOONER or later any geologist nowadays may find himself using air photographs, if only in quite elementary ways. If, for example, he is working in an area of badly exposed rocks, he may use them as a means of finding outcrops. Again, in thinly populated areas, such as the Scottish Highlands, the published topographical maps may carry so little detail that he is obliged to take photographs into the field as a substitute.

The real importance of air photographs to geologists, however, lies in their use as primary sources of geological information. There are, of course, many important kinds of information which could never be obtained by this means. It is obvious, for example, that a personal visit is needed if anything is to be discovered about the fossils in a bed of sedimentary rock, or about the exact composition and detailed structures of a rock of any kind. Nevertheless, provided an area is not too thickly covered with superficial deposits or vegetation, air photographs will generally reveal most large-scale geological features, and may thus provide a means of establishing not only the existence of these features but also their exact location and extent.

It is true that a field geologist with enough time to spare would eventually extract from an area all that air photographs could tell him and a good deal more. Time, however, is an important consideration. Air photographs may tell the geologist nothing about small features, but they may very rapidly provide him with all the information he needs about the larger features. Thus, it is generally possible to produce an outline geological map only a few days after the photographs have been taken. The map will indeed be incomplete, for the exact age and nature of the rocks will usually be indeterminable and some parts of the area may be altogether concealed. Nevertheless, if prepared by a skilled interpreter it will be accurate within its own limitations.

Hence air photographs are now indispensable to all geological surveyors, whether academic, commercial or in government service.

Ideally they are used in conjunction with field-surveys, each source of information being used as a check upon the other. Sometimes, however, if time is pressing and the area difficult of access, a map may actually be prepared and brought into use long before a ground-survey has been completed. There may not even be a map, for as a temporary measure it may be enough merely to show the information on a photographic mosaic.

Vertical cover with stereoscopic overlap is most commonly used in geological surveying. Generally this is of much smaller scale than the photographs in use for most other kinds of photographic interpretation: large-scale photographs will not only increase the cost of covering a given area but may actually obscure the existence of regional trends and features. Thus a scale of 1 : 20,000 is considered 'large', while scales of 1 : 50,000 or even less are not at all unusual. Obliques are of

---

Plate 13.   Pen-yr-Afr, North Pembrokeshire (SN120486).

Low oblique views can sometimes provide far more geological information than vertical photographs. Most of the area is a level plateau with a thin but continuous cover of drift. A vertical air photograph could well give the impression that the underlying bedrock was of simple structure. Oblique views, however, reveal the steep coastal cliffs, which provide excellent sections showing that the rocks beneath the plateau are in fact intensely folded.

In country where most of the outcrops occur on very steep slopes, the use of oblique photographs may be the only practicable way of obtaining exact information about geological structures. A detailed examination of the cliffs of Pen-yr-Afr would certainly be very laborious and would probably require some mountaineering ability. The point is even more obvious where the outcrops occur on the slopes of high and inaccessible mountains.

GZ 7

19 July 1951

Plate 13.   Pen-yr-Afr

limited value, as they cannot normally be viewed stereoscopically and may also include areas of 'dead ground'. There is, however, one purpose for which they alone can be used: the study of outcrops on very steep slopes (see Plate 13).

The interpretation of the photographs is a process similar in many ways to the collection of information on the ground, though of course far quicker. First, boundaries between outcrops of different kinds of rocks must be marked off, in so far as they can be distinguished. Next, if the outcrops are discontinuous, as a result of faulting, erosion or any other cause, some attempt must be made at correlation. That is to say, it must be decided which of the detached outcrops, if any, belong in reality to the same bodies of rock. In the field this would be done largely by the recognition of lithological details, with additional help from fossils in the case of many sedimentary rocks. Such methods are of course impossible with air photographs, but combinations of tone and texture on the photographic print will generally serve the same purpose. A cover of vegetation may actually be an advantage, for a given rock type may support its own particular flora which may have a characteristic appearance on the photographs.

All this may be done without any attempt on the part of the interpreter to name, or even describe, the rocks which he is studying. To do so, indeed, would often involve straining the evidence or be impossible, but there are cases where a rock can be placed within some general category. For example, if an outcrop is easily eroded, carries pools of standing water and has given rise to mudflows or landslips, it must be composed of shale or clay. Again, country containing closed depressions, dry valleys and other signs of underground drainage, is almost certainly composed of limestone or dolomite (Plate 14).

Once the pattern of outcrops has been established, structural features can then be examined. Faults may be immediately obvious: if exposed, they appear as displacements of outcrops: if concealed, their courses may still be deduced from topographical features such as scarps or valleys (Plate 15). The directions in which sedimentary strata are inclined can easily be determined, and with a little trouble even the angle of the dip may be estimated with reasonable accuracy. In addition it may be possible to establish the patterns made by structures which are small but of regional importance, such as joints, cleavages and the lineations of metamorphic rocks (Plates 14 and 16).

Thus within a very short time all the major structural features of an area (cf. Plate 17), and many minor ones, may be revealed. This is perhaps the most important of all geological applications of air photographs, for the collection of such information on the ground is a particularly long and laborious process.

Little has been said so far about the interpretation of topographical features, except as an aid to the identification of rock-types and the location of structures. In one branch of geology, however, it is of supreme importance. This is Quaternary geology, which deals with events during and since the last ice-age.

At the present day, given processes of erosion can be seen to produce particular topographical forms (cf. e.g. Plates 16 and 18), and the same is true of processes of deposition. This must have been so since the earth first became solid, but in general a form that owes its origin to one process is unlikely to survive for long before being greatly modified or destroyed by another. Forms produced during the last million years may still, however, be partially or wholly preserved, and may bear witness to geological events for which no other evidence exists. Thus, when a

(continued on p. 50.)

Plate 14. The Burren, near Black Head, Co. Clare, Eire.
This is an area of flat-topped, steep-sided hills, separated by deep valleys. For the most part the hill-sides are terraced. Each terrace represents the outcrop of a particular bed of rock, and since each appears to follow the contours the beds themselves must be nearly horizontal.

The photograph illustrates two points particularly well. Firstly, most of the valleys can be seen to lack streams. In an area of high rainfall this means that most of the drainage is underground, which in turn indicates that the rock is limestone. This is confirmed by the presence of several small closed depressions, the largest of which, elliptical in shape, is conspicuous near the centre of the photograph. These are solution-hollows, among the most distinctive features of limestone areas. Secondly, all the areas of bare rock are scored with fine parallel lines running across the photograph (not to be confused with the numerous stone walls). As they run straight across country, disregarding the topography, they must be the outcrops of vertical planes, but since they do not disrupt the beds they cannot be faults. They are in fact joints; planes along which the rocks have broken but without much displacement. Joints are caused by regional stress, often, as in this case, too weak to cause folding or faulting, and may therefore provide valuable information about the dynamic history of an area. It is obviously important to measure their orientations, and this can often be done as easily from air photographs as on the ground, and in a much shorter time.
Vertical photograph supplied by Ambassador Irish Oil Co., Eire 62 1 Run 2, print No. 9023. Scale 1 : 19,000   *14 April 1962*

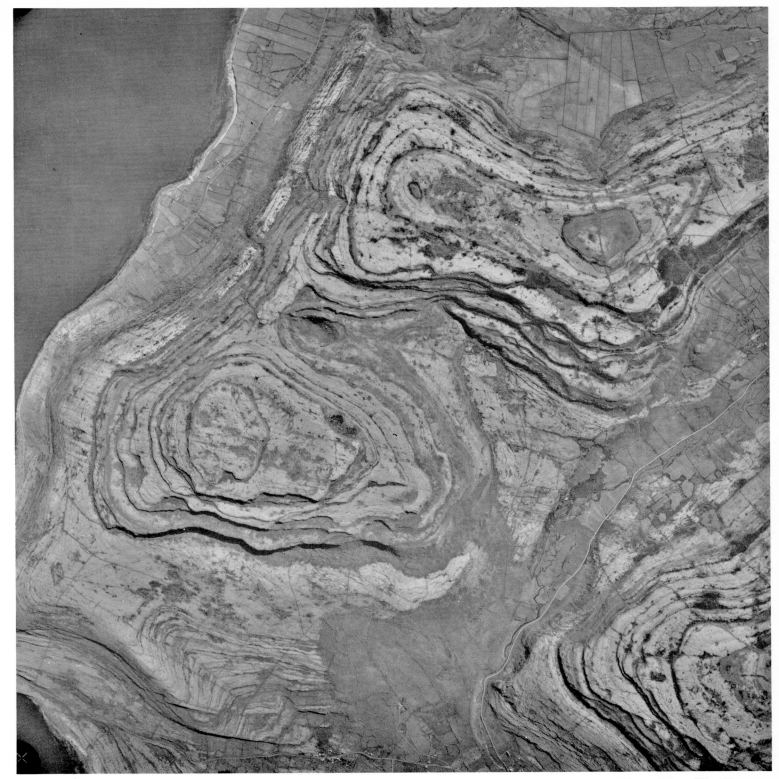

Plate 14.   The Burren

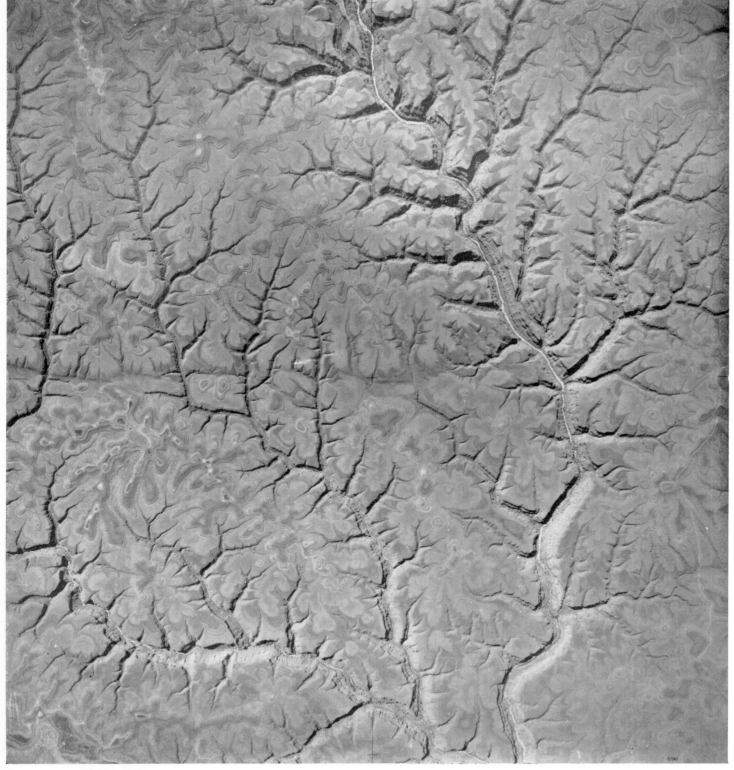

Plate 15. This area in the Aden Protectorate is a plateau cut out by a network of gorges, some deep and steep-sided. There is a little vegetation in the gorges but virtually none on the plateau itself. Apart from the gorges, the most obvious features on the photograph are the bands and patches of different shades of grey, the bands being arranged in parallel sets forming irregular closed loops. These mark the outcrops of different beds of rock. They are so well exposed and so distinctive in appearance that a fairly detailed geological map could be prepared from this photograph alone.

Even without a stereoscope it is easy to see that the beds throughout the area lie almost horizontally. The clue is given by the outcrops on the sides of the gorges, which form alternate cliffs and ledges continuing for great distances without much change of level. This accounts for the fact that the pattern of outcrops resembles a pattern of contour-lines on a topographical map; the outcrops do indeed follow the contour-lines round small hills.

One other feature of structural interest is revealed by the drainage-pattern. For the most part this is irregular, but it can be seen that several small tributary valleys have disposed themselves along a single almost straight line, running across the centre of the photograph. This must be a line of weakness, and stereoscopic examination shows that it is in fact a fault, the rocks on the side nearer the top of the photograph having been shifted relatively downwards. The displacement is small and can hardly be detected on this single small-scale photograph. Nevertheless, such an alignment would at once strike an interpreter as being worthy of close attention.
R.A.F. vertical photograph V540/RAF/1751, print No. 0025.
Scale 1 : 79,400   *26 November 1955*

Plate 15. Dissected plateau

Plate 16. *Zambia, 40 miles SE. of Mazabuka. The photograph shows a broad flat-bottomed valley bounded on one side by a plateau (top right) and on the other side by a narrow range of hills. Most of the area is thickly wooded and little bare rock is visible, but it is still possible to reach certain conclusions about the geology.*

The strong resemblance between the 'textures' of the two upland areas, with their strong corrugations, suggests that both are carved out of the same series of rocks. The corrugations themselves clearly denote regular alternations of relatively hard and less resistant beds, and their straight courses imply very steep dips. Only in the right-hand half of the plateau do the corrugations show a tendency to deviate from the straight, indicating a more gentle dip towards the left.

The large central valley can hardly be a simple erosional feature, as it cuts right across the structures of the upland areas. In fact, the long escarpment which forms its upper margin is so straight and steep that it can only be a fault-scarp, and the same conclusion is suggested by the appearance of the opposite escarpment as seen on adjacent photographs in the series. This, then, is a rift-valley, formed by the lowering of a narrow belt of the earth's crust between two great parallel fractures.

Moreover, a close examination of the valley floor shows that it does not, as might be expected, consist merely of modern alluvium overlying the same upturned rocks as those of the plateau. First of all, the conspicuous eye-shaped feature near its lower border can be seen (with a stereoscope) to be an abrupt downfold, forming a structural basin unmatched in the upland areas. In addition, faint parallel lines are visible in places which can be seen (again with a stereoscope) to be a series of outcrops running in an entirely different direction from those of the plateau. Thus, it appears that the rocks forming the valley-floor belong to some quite different series, presumably underlain by the 'plateau rocks' at depth. The inference is that these newer rocks formerly covered the whole area, but have been removed by erosion except where they have been preserved by down-faulting.

The history of the area would thus seem to have been as follows. First, the 'plateau rocks' were intensely folded in the 'north-south' direction. After considerable erosion, another series of rocks was laid down upon them. Faulting then occurred, itself perhaps responsible for the gentle folding of the younger rocks now only seen in the valley floor. Subsequent erosion has completely removed these rocks from the upland areas, but they remain on the floor of the fault-valley where they have been relatively protected.

R.A.F. vertical photograph 82E/382/3, print No. 5072.
Scale 1 : 35,000   *June 1951*

Plate 16.   Geological structures, Zambia

glacier erodes a valley it produces certain topographical features which may still be recognisable long after the glacier has melted. Similarly the cliff and wave-cut platform of a marine shore-line may survive even though the sea-level has sunk or the land risen, and the form of ancient sand-dunes in desert areas may denote wind-directions different from those of the present time.

As with the 'solid' geology, all such features can of course be studied perfectly well without air photographs, and indeed the ideal procedure is always to carry out an orthodox topographical survey. Once again, however, the stereoscopic use of air photographs allows the investigation to be undertaken far more rapidly, if less accurately and perhaps with the loss of some detail. The method is particularly simple when a plan of the feature is all that is needed, but by the use of photogrammetric techniques contour-lines may generally be added if necessary.

It is also worth mentioning that many features of geomorphological interest are defined by such small changes of level and slope that an observer on the ground might be unaware of their very existence. Air photographs, however, when viewed stereoscopically, enable the ground to be seen in greatly exaggerated relief. Hence, their use may lead to the discovery of subdued geomorphological features the existence of which had never been suspected, even in areas which are perfectly easy of access.

That the geological interpretation of air photographs depends very largely upon stereoscopic examination will now be abundantly clear. Since it is difficult to present pairs of stereoscopic photographs in a book, the illustrations here have been carefully chosen to show geological features without resource to a stereoscope. It must be emphasised, however, that they would yield far more information if viewed stereoscopically, and that most individual small-scale photographs provide little geological information of any value.

Plate 17. Kenya, 100 miles NNE. of Nanyuki. This is a gently undulating area with a few broad and shallow stream-beds, most of them dry. Trees grow fairly thickly in some of the stream-beds but are elsewhere very scattered.

Throughout most of the area the ground is marked with fine parallel lines, and close inspection shows that these are very narrow ridges, made conspicuous by their shadows. They are the outcrops of the more resistant beds of rock, and from their disposition much can be learned about the structure of the area. Firstly, they can be seen to continue across the valleys without the slightest deviation. This means that the beds themselves must be standing nearly vertical. Secondly, though not deflected by topographical features, they do nevertheless describe great sweeping curves. In other words, the beds have not only been tipped-up vertically but have also been folded. All this must have happened in the very remote past, as the whole area has since been almost flattened by erosion.

The most conspicuous of all the features on the photograph, however, are the four irregular dark patches. These are volcanic cones with their associated lava-flows; this is especially obvious in the case of the one nearest the top of the photograph. All must be of recent date, as they still retain much of their original form. In addition, a narrow dark band can be seen running alongside the river near the left-hand edge of the photograph. This is another lava-flow which has evidently run down the valley, displacing the river as it did so. Some trees have already grown on its surface, which shows that it must be somewhat older than most of the lava-flows associated with the cones.

R.A.F. vertical photograph 15 KE/30 print No. 028. Scale 1 : 38,850
30 February 1956

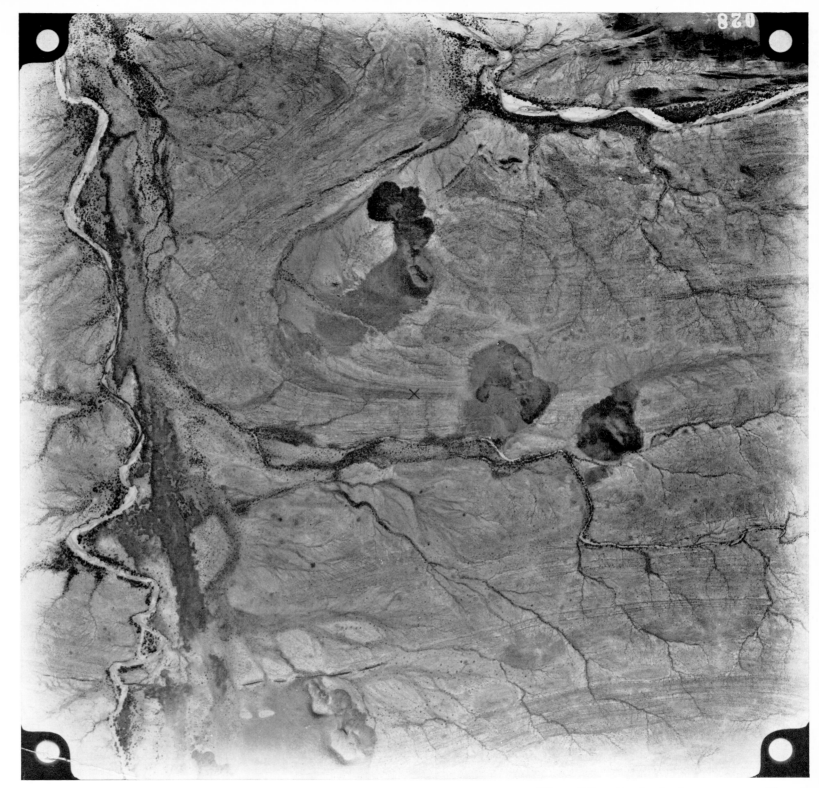

Plate 17. Geological structures, Kenya

Plate 18. Glen Roy, Inverness-shire (NN303887).
The main valley shown on the photograph is Glen Roy,
which is flanked on either side by mountains of the
Grampian Highlands. Most of the area is covered with
peat and drift deposits, and there is a good deal of low
vegetation. For this reason the photograph provides little
information about the solid rocks, except that they must
be hard enough to stand up as steep slopes. They are in
fact metamorphic rocks of Pre-Cambrian age, intensely
disturbed by earth-movements.

The outstanding interest of the photograph lies in
the series of three parallel lines visible on both sides of
the valley, those on the left-hand side being especially
continuous and distinct. These are the so called 'parallel
roads' of Glen Roy, each of which is in reality a narrow
ledge, horizontal throughout its length. Long ago these
were recognised as ancient shore-lines, representing successive levels of an ice-dammed lake which at one time
filled the valley and its tributaries; eventually, evidence
was found to show that the lake owed its existence to a
shrinking glacier which once occupied the lower part of
the valley. A set of photographs covering the whole area
would enable a map of the complete system to be made,
while photogrammetry would demonstrate the horizon-
tality of the 'roads' and give an estimate of their altitudes.
In this way a geologist, without ever having visited Glen
Roy, would be in a position not only to deduce the former
existence of the lake but also to state its levels and extent
at different stages.
R.A.F. vertical photograph CPE/SCOT. UK 177, print
No. 3253.
Scale 1 : 11,800   7 October 1947

Plate 18.   Glacial Lake beaches

J. A. STEERS

Air Photographs and the Geographer

TO the geographer, whether he is interested in the physical or the human side of the subject, air photographs are a most useful aid in his work. In general the vertical photograph is the more valuable since, if the height at which it was taken and the focal length of the camera are known, or if certain features on the picture are easily identifiable, a mean scale may be added and the picture used as an approximate map. On the other hand an oblique picture may often give a much more vivid representation of the ground. At the present time most air photographs are black and white. The obvious limitation of expense governs this. A black and white picture can, however, give a great deal of information about the nature of the ground and its plant cover. The detail is far more readily appreciated if, as is nearly always the case, overlapping photographs are taken so that they can be viewed stereoscopically. In this way not only the details of the land, but the vegetation and all other features can be seen in three dimensions. Naturally, the larger the scale of the photographs, the greater the possibility of appreciating small details. If colour photographs are available, the effect is far more striking. Unfortunately, the cost of colour photography is high, but there is no doubt that coloured photographs in stereo-pairs offer great advantages. This is perhaps a more significant point than at first appears since physiography and ecology are almost inseparable in understanding landscape, and colour shows variations in terrain and vegetation so much more clearly and accurately, giving the effect of a natural landscape.

Some aspects of coastal research illustrate the inter-relation of ground form and plant cover to great advantage. On a marsh coast small differences of relief are of great significance. The tidal range varies from place to place. On parts of the north Norfolk coast it is about 20 feet at springs; thus, except for wind-blown dunes and shingle ridges piled up by the waves, the relief is more or less confined within that range. The nature of the ground may vary from clean sand, through sand thinly covered by mud, thick mud which may be compact or very wet, to mud encroaching on shingle. Vegetation may cover all or nearly all the mud, and often much of the sand and shingle. The nature of the vegetation will depend not only on the surface on which it is growing, but also on the number of times it is covered by tidal waters. In other words there will be a noteworthy change from the plants at levels covered by all high waters to those only reached by exceptional tides. Moreover, the pattern of marsh physiography is intricate (Plate 11). The creeks wind about and have many branches; their sides are generally steep in old marsh, but in young, developing marsh they are far less well-defined. The shingle and sand ridges which usually border a marsh on one or more sides are low, and may pass under the mud at one edge and elsewhere may be dune-covered. They may also carry vegetation. All these features are far more clearly viewed and appreciated in an air photograph. Their pattern becomes clear; the variation in the vegetation will be seen to vary with slight changes in the nature and height of the surface; parts which are being washed away and others which are being built up will be readily identified. The different plants can usually be easily recognised on a black and white photograph, partly by their form, partly by slight differences of tone, and also because of their position relative to creeks, sand or shingle. But the whole marsh becomes alive if seen in colour. There is also another great advantage that an aerial view, whether vertical or oblique, possesses in flat country—it allows a wide sweep of detail impossible to see at ground level. The branching of creeks and the divagations of shingle ridges take on a new meaning.

Similar advantages are found in photographs of almost any terrain. A mountain landscape becomes far more intelligible; each small valley, cirque, arête, moraine, whatever it may be, is seen in relation to its environment (Plate 19). The more difficult a tract of country is to traverse, the more helpful is the air photograph. An extreme example is the limestone area known as the Cockpit Country in Jamaica. Recent work in

53

the Polar regions has shown the tremendous help that air photography can give to the explorer. There is no need to expand on this, but one point must be made—the photograph cannot fully replace the knowledge to be gained from a study of the ground itself. It may help enormously, and it may well provide the key to some difficult problem. Nevertheless, the combination of careful field work with good air photographs, both vertical and oblique, is nearly always necessary if a full understanding is desired. On the other hand, for reconnaissance work, for planning details of ground research and for many other reasons, a detailed study of air photographs is a necessary preliminary.

The physiographer often needs either to make a map of the area he is studying or to insert on a published map the features with which he is concerned. Existing maps, whether those of our own Ordnance Survey or of corresponding bodies in other countries, are concerned mainly with representation of the topography. In many places no maps at all exist. To make an accurate map requires a good deal of time, and this is not always available. A vertical photograph is of great help, and certain impressions can only be obtained in this way. Some years before the war of 1939-45, when working on the Great Barrier Reefs of Queensland, I was much concerned with various features including cays and low-wooded islands. Both in 1928 and in 1936 air photographs of the reefs were almost unobtainable, and since some of the islands, although small, were thickly covered by shrubs and trees, the only way to map them was by means of a closed traverse. Recently I have had discussions with a colleague who has been investigating the reefs of British Honduras where similar types of island occur. His air photographs are a revelation. The same is true in all types of physiographical work where a bird's eye view is required.

Since an air photograph can be taken at any time provided an aircraft is available, and light and weather conditions are suitable, the method is of particular value in recording changes that take place rapidly. In physical geography the changes wrought by a volcano, a severe earthquake, a great flood, or by a storm on the coast can all be recorded. If a map or photographic cover of the area affected already exists, the amount of change may be readily seen, and may even be measured, if photographs are taken with stereoscopic overlap. In this country we are not by any means free from catastrophic changes; air photographs recording the effects of the great tidal surge on the east coast in 1953 are most revealing. Pictures showing the effects of the Exmoor floods in 1952, and those that dislocated rail and road traffic between Edinburgh and the Border in 1948, are of great interest. Reference has already been made to salt-marshes. If a contoured map is required of them, no better means is available than a series of vertical air photographs taken at short intervals during a rising tide. With reasonable ground control a map with a vertical interval of a foot or even less, is possible.

Change, however, is by no means always produced by natural agencies. Modern earth-moving machinery can cause great alterations in a short time. The effects of open-cast mining are well known, but their true significance is best appreciated from the air. Similarly, the artificial exposures made in gravel beds in river valleys, and the unfortunate effects produced on the landscape, are made abundantly clear. Man-made changes are nowadays so rapid and often so devastating that a proper record is desirable, and no other method is more readily applicable than air photography. Open-cast mining and gravel pits are but two aspects of the whole problem of mineral working (Plates 20, 21). Almost always the immediate effect on the land is depressing and the changes that follow the excavation of clay for brick-making may be profound. A journey by road along the outcrop of the Oxford Clay is revealing; a flight in a helicopter makes the scale of operations far plainer. The replacement of cover and top soil may help to restore the countryside, but photographs should be taken before and after the extraction to allow a proper and permanent record of the changes and, consequently, to afford evidence of the ill effects that can be avoided in a future enterprise.

Mineral working is only a part of the far greater and vital problem of land use. Maps can never keep pace with the rapid changes which take place nowadays. The land utilisation surveys of the 1930s and of the 1960s are essential documents if we wish to understand our own country. Despite the careful organisation set up and the zeal of a great number of individuals who did the actual mapping, each survey inevitably extended over a period of years. If it had been practicable to do the surveys by air the time taken would have been far less and they would have been representative of a much shorter period. Moreover, for selected areas, yearly surveys could have been made. This comment in no sense belittles the two ground surveys. They have made known not only the use and misuse of our land, but also have demonstrated how

---

Plate 19. Panorama looking east over Ruadh Stac to Garbh-Bheinn (NG532232), Skye. Such comprehensive views of mountainous landscape can seldom be obtained from a point on the ground.
AGM 75   *24 June 1962*

Plate 19.   Panorama of Strath na-Creitheach

Plate 20. Open-cast coal workings, Stainborough, Yorkshire, W.R. (SE322024). Apart from the immediate loss of amenities, such open-cast workings for iron or coal cause changes that persist long after the area has been reconditioned, for the levelled ground never returns to its original geological compactness. EE 73   23 July 1949

Plate 20.   Open-cast coal workings

Plate 21. Gravel pits (SU570957), Thames valley, north of Dorchester, Oxfordshire. Since 1949, when this photograph was taken, operations have extended over the entire area to left of the main road. Near the centre of the photograph an archaeological site is being excavated in advance of destruction.
CB 133   *11 April 1949*

Plate 21.   Gravel pits

important it is that we should be prepared to have air surveys so that a proper appreciation of change in land use can be obtained.

Land use is a wide term and includes, for example, irrigation and artificial drainage schemes, factory lay-outs, especially those of large plants, steel works and power-stations. The channelling of transport by road, rail, and canal can often be best envisaged on air mosaics. It is, of course, true that all these, and many other features too, can be mapped in the ordinary way, but once again it must be emphasised that with the speed at which change takes place today it is seldom, if ever, possible to keep pace, by ordinary methods of map production, with the changing uses to which land is put. Moreover, we live in an age of planning, and a great many people who may not always be familiar with the uses and limitations of surface maps are concerned with the future of our country-side and cities. There is no doubt that air photographs, individually or as mosaics, may enable many intelligent persons to understand not only better, but also more readily and easily, what is happening. The photograph allows a perspective approach which is by no means always attainable on the ground.

In many parts of the world maps are scarce or non-existent, and even, as in the United States, where they are available, the effect of gulley erosion and consequent loss of soil are more strikingly brought out by air photographs than in any other way. Soil erosion is, however, not confined to mapped countries; it is all too common in many lands. Its nature and effects, and the rapid changes that take place from year to year, or even in much shorter periods, can be seen at once on photographs, a proper study of which may well indicate the nature of the remedial measures which should be adopted to check the loss. In areas subject to soil erosion preliminary reconnaissance from the air may well be of great practical value, in, for instance, directing the lines of future development, whether of settlement, or the tracks of roads and railways.

A colleague of mine has been concerned recently with land use in parts of south-east Brazil. Maps were inadequate, since they were on a scale of 1 : 1,000,000 which was of little use for field work. On the other hand, very fair air cover was available for considerable areas, and at a scale of 1 : 25,000. The value of aerial photographs is, in fact, well illustrated in Brazil, a country larger than the United States. About 70 per cent is photographed (1963) but less than 10 per cent is mapped! Only a cursory glance at an atlas showing the Eastern Highlands, the great Amazonian plains, and the Andes in the west, is necessary to appreciate the significance of these percentages. In his work Mr P. Haggett found that in the field the photographs had three main uses—

the fixing of position, the identification of features, and for help in the final checking of work already done on the photographs in the laboratory. He also noted an interesting point: local farmers intuitively recognised features on air photographs far more easily than on printed maps. The conventions on maps were apt to confuse those unfamiliar with their use, whereas air photographs show things as they are. In the laboratory the pictures were also of great value. It was not possible to visit all parts of an extensive area, so use was made of a statistical convention, i.e. stratified random sampling, to select survey points representative of the area. Then, by means of stereoscopic pairs, these sampled areas could be classified, slopes measured, the nature of forest identified, including the forest canopy, and sheet and gulley erosion evaluated. Thus a relatively reliable picture could be built up. In addition, certain direct measurements of vegetation-height, of angles of slope, and other features could be made. Thus, the photographs made possible the assessment of a wide area in a short time, and also allowed comparisons of land use to be made at frequent intervals. A geologist can collect rocks, a botanist plants, but a geographer cannot collect landscapes; he can capture a landscape at a given point in time on a picture, and bring the picture back for analysis. 'At a given moment' is an important proviso. The country looks very different in summer and winter, at sunrise and sunset and at midday, in cloudy and in clear weather. Some features, especially those which are the result of man's handiwork, are far more visible in certain lights than at other times. Long shadows often accentuate some features whereas nearly vertical light may emphasise others.

It will be clear from what has been said that changes of land use have their effects on the surface, and that these changes show up in air photographs. Other chapters in this book show how the archaeologist is helped; ancient settlements, former roads, causeways and many other man-made items can be readily identified from the air. *A fortiori*, more recent changes are often more easily traced and so the historical geographer has in air photographs a most valuable tool. In this sense, as well as in others, historical geography is only recent archaeology, but it

---

Plate 22. Fenland landscape (TL613849), panorama of peat fens south-east of Littleport, Cambridgeshire, looking east. The original course of the Little Ouse is seen as a roddon, a meandering bank of silt visible by reason of its light colour which contrasts with the black peaty soil elsewhere. WL 2   *5 June 1958*

Plate 22. Fenland landscape

Plate 23. Bury St Edmunds (TL854642), Suffolk, looking north. To the left of the abbey precinct lies the grid of streets of the town founded by Abbot Baldwin in the eleventh century.
HO 67   19 June 1952

Plate 24. The village of Trumpington (TL443549), two miles south of Cambridge. The nucleus of the village lies round the parish church; ribbon-development has taken place along the main road, and there is a modern (1948-50) housing-estate in the distance.
WU 97   30 June 1958

Plate 23.   Bury St Edmunds

Plate 24. Trumpington

comes within the historic period during which there was much alteration in our own land, even before the Industrial Revolution. Research into lost villages is but one rewarding line of enquiry that can be studied with profit from the air, as is shown by recent work in the Midlands and in East Anglia (Plate 64). Air photographs clearly reveal the absence of village settlement on the marshes of the estuaries, whereas the numerous villages along the lower valleys and the far fewer hamlets on the lower divides, give great scope for discussion on the spread of colonisation in the region. Few other parts of the world have been so intensively studied from the air as the Fenland of eastern England (Plate 22). The information so gathered has enabled archaeologists and historians to piece together the history of man's occupation of the Fens in great detail, and fresh information is continually coming to light.

We know that most of the boulder-clay country of East Anglia was formerly forested; in some ways it must have resembled the Wealden area of Sussex where air photographs strikingly emphasise the differences between the early settlement of the downland, the coastal plain, and the Weald. Not only is the density of settlement brought out, but also variations in the nature of this settlement, the patterns of fields and field-systems, as well as that of the villages themselves. On the ground many of these phenomena are not apparent. Even so simple a correlation as that which locally exists between present hedge-lines and old field-boundaries and strips as shown on estate maps of the seventeenth and eighteenth centuries is best demonstrated by a vertical view. An inference which may justifiably be drawn from this is that air photographs may throw light also on pre-enclosure field patterns. In the same way former tracks and roads, footpaths and bridle-ways, may be readily identified, whereas on the ground, although some stretches may remain, others have disappeared under crops or have been built over. Man-made features on the surface may be discontinuous and confusing, so that their meaning is far from clear. During recent investigations of the Broads, which finally established their artificial origin, air photography revealed the true significance of certain features of this kind which proved to mark former property-boundaries.

The bird's eye view, used intelligently, may also reveal the essence of a pattern which is obscured in all sorts of ways to an investigator on the ground. As examples, in London the significance of the relationship between the City and Westminster is made clear, while in Edinburgh the importance of the High Street, the Castle, Holyrood, and the New Town are admirably brought out. On a smaller scale a notable example of medieval town planning can be seen at Bury St. Edmunds (Plate 23). Study of a map, or even careful ground inspection, cannot reveal these points so effectively. The structure of villages is often beautifully displayed from the air. Thus the three main stages in the growth of Trumpington, in Cambridgeshire, jump to the eye. Plate 24 shows the original settlement around the church, the later ribbon development along the main road, and the planned development of the present day.

There is no need to enumerate in further detail the many ways in which air photographs are of service to geographers. Whatever the particular nature of a piece of field work may be it is more than probable that the investigation will be helped by adequate photographic cover. Much that cannot possibly be recorded in any other way is directly obtainable from air photographs, but it must be emphasised that, wherever practicable, the information yielded must be checked on the ground; the more frequently this is done the less chance there is of mistakes arising in the interpretation of photographs of inaccessible localities. The geographer so often needs more than a map showing a particular place at a particular date; the map cannot be quickly made or re-made; the photograph can, however, be re-taken as often as is necessary. Thus the constant changes taking place are recorded, and the investigator has available far more evidence than can usually be obtained from the ground. In certain types of country it is really the only means of adequate record. The growth or regression of a sand or shingle spit; the changing patterns of a braided stream; the evolution of a new volcano or lava flow,[1] and the subsequent spread of vegetation over them; the profound changes in big cities since the war of 1939-45; the varying flow of traffic in rural and urban areas, are but a few of the phenomena that can be studied more quickly and effectively by means of air photographs.

NOTE

[1] The recent film of Tristan da Cunha illustrates this point admirably.

R. M. S. PERRIN

Air Photography and the Scientific Study of Soils

THE scientific study of soils, or pedology, is concerned firstly with the morphology, classification and distribution of soils (normally studied in vertical sections or 'profiles'), and secondly with the elucidation, as far as possible in quantitative terms, of processes occurring in them. The contribution of air photography is limited to recording the distribution of soils, but this has a value extending beyond pedology itself to its practical applications in the control of soil fertility and erosion, in inventories of natural resources, in land-use planning and in civil engineering. The bibliography of the applications and techniques of air photography in soil studies is now very large[1] and it would be impossible to review it adequately in the present short chapter. Examples have therefore been restricted largely to basic pedological work and chosen, for convenience, from research in progress at Cambridge.

The use of air photographs takes two main forms—reconnaissance and mapping.

RECONNAISSANCE

The object of air reconnaissance is to obtain information of features either unknown, or only imperfectly known, from ground observation; such features observed from the air may then be recorded by photography. Alternatively, new information may be gleaned by search of existing photographic cover, not necessarily obtained specifically for the purpose. Either vertical or oblique photography is suitable, but in practice new observations are more easily, speedily and cheaply recorded as oblique views. These are also often the most suitable material for teaching or exhibition purposes as they are more readily understood by the non-specialist. Routine search of existing cover is almost invariably carried out on vertical photographs. Wherever possible photographs taken at different seasons should be consulted, as soil phenomena may be recorded either by colour differences in bare ground,

which vary with moisture, or by patterns in natural vegetation and crops, which may react differentially to moisture or show seasonal aspects.

Air photography is here a research tool of unique value as is demonstrated by Plates 25 and 26. These show soil and vegetation patterns in the Breckland district of East Anglia considered to be due to periglacial disturbance in the soil profile. Although their existence was already known from ground observation,[2] many details of the patterns and their extent and distribution were not appreciated until air reconnaissance was applied.[3] Morphologically similar patterns have also been observed on the Chalk in northern France. They are almost certainly of the same origin as those shown in Plates 25 and 26 but their existence was quite unknown until they were revealed for the first time by air reconnaissance.[4]

Such discoveries must, of course, always be followed up with field investigations but the selection of critical sites at which to prepare sections and of the direction in which they should be cut will be considerably facilitated by prior study of air photographs.

MAPPING

While the results of reconnaissance may be spectacular, the main contribution of air photography to pedology is in soil mapping.

Air Photographs as a Base Map

The simplest and most obvious application is in providing a base map where printed topographic maps are either lacking, insufficiently detailed or obsolete. This use is self-evident in regions such as desert, muskeg or tropical rain-forest, but it can be very important, even in well-mapped countries such as Britain, in wooded areas, moorland or marsh, where large-scale maps either carry insufficient detail or very quickly become out of date. The surveyor will use the photographs

(Continued on page 66)

Plate 25. Soil patterns

Plate 25. Soil patterns in arable fields at Kilverstone, Norfolk (TL894844). These patterns are very characteristic of the Breckland district where thin sandy drift overlies the Chalk. They may be revealed by differences in colour of the soil, as here, by patterns in natural vegetation (Plate 26) or by differential growth of crops. On plateau sites they are reticulate (A), with increasing slope they become vermicular (B) and then elongated (C).

Where sections have been cut across the patterns they are found to be associated with very characteristic disturbances below the surface. Typically these consist of alternate ridges or pillars of very chalky drift and deep troughs or pockets filled with loose sand. The underlying system of sandy troughs and chalky ridges is shown up in favourable cases by the contrasting colours of the materials brought to the surface by ploughing.

Air photography is not an infallible tool in the study of these phenomena. The patterns may not be recorded unless the photographs are taken at the right season. Where the surface soil is moderately heavy, the patterns are generally not developed.

RS 84   23 March 1956

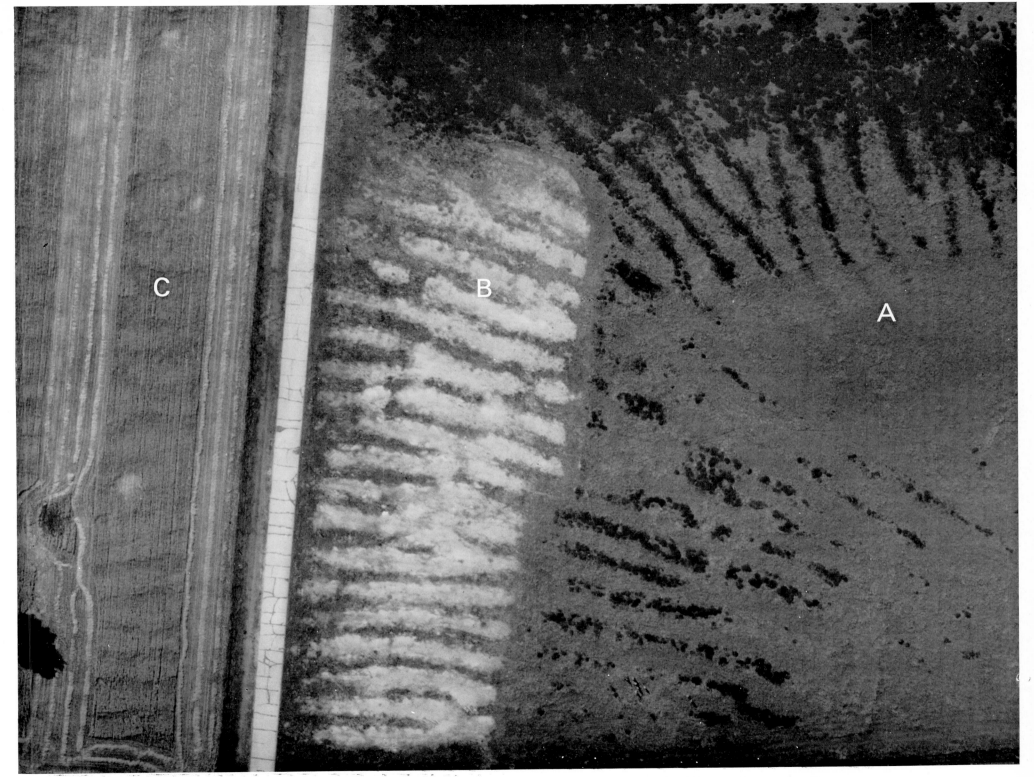

Plate 26. Vegetation and soil patterns *(for explanation see page 66)*

both for fixing his position in the field and for recording his observations. Boundaries may subsequently be transferred to a printed map; or alternatively mosaics may be prepared from the photographs, which are then reproduced as half-tone plates overprinted with the soil data. This method is extensively used by the U.S. Soil Survey in numerous recent memoirs and is illustrated in Plate 29. A map of this type can be produced rapidly and cheaply and in featureless terrain is often more readily comprehended by the layman.

Only recent vertical photographs of high quality are normally suitable as base maps. Overlap should be sufficient (ideally about 66 per cent) to allow complete stereo-vision over the whole field. This is particularly important in difficult terrain as an aid to accurate fixing and plotting.

Plates 27 and 28 illustrate the use of vertical photographs as a base map, as used by D. A. MacLeod in current studies on the genesis and reclamation of soils on salt-marsh along the margin of the Wash. In these marshes the pattern of creeks, levees and salt-pans is extremely complex and ever-changing (cf., e.g., Plates 27a and 27b), and good landmarks for easily fixing position by resection are lacking; thus, there is no substitute for up-to-date vertical photographs for finding one's

way across the marsh, for fixing accurately the position of soil-profile pits, and for recording soil boundaries traced on the ground.

Direct Mapping of Soils

Soil profiles as such cannot, of course, be observed on air photographs. *Direct* mapping by this means is therefore only possible when different surface soils within the area are recorded by contrasting tones on the photographs. Such contrasts, only observable in the virtual absence of vegetation (in deserts, some savannahs, eroded or cultivated ground), are due either to differences in *chemical* or *mineralogical composition* (e.g. amounts of calcium carbonate, free oxides of iron, pale-coloured stones, crystallised salts or organic matter); or to differences in *moisture*, caused jointly by the factors of permeability (related to particle size distribution and pore-space relationships) and topographic situation. This represents a restricted catalogue of soil properties, so that direct mapping is confined to specially favourable circumstances. Furthermore, even when tonal differences are observed in bare ground, they cannot always be related unambiguously to differences in profile morphology.

As when photographs are used as base maps, only recent vertical cover of high quality is acceptable and this must be obtained at the season when maximum tonal contrast can be expected. Even at the optimum season a certain amount of luck is involved since some tonal differences are only recorded in certain lighting conditions. Much routine cover obtained for purposes other than soil mapping may thus prove useless. Oblique photographs find little scientific application owing to the difficulties involved in correcting to the horizontal, although they may have a limited use in illustrating reports.

Photographs for direct mapping have hitherto been commonly on panchromatic film. Infra-red film can be valuable for recognising differences in moisture content, but with all black and white photographs ambiguity arises in relating shades of grey on the print to actual colours on the surface, and in distinguishing tones due in reality to thin cover of vegetation. In spite of present high costs, colour film has obvious advantages here, which will encourage its greater use in future.

R. S. Seale of the Soil Survey of England and Wales has recently used air photography for precise direct mapping of restricted areas of soils in the Fens. Plates 29 and 30 illustrate the method and indicate some circumstances in which it breaks down. Patterns similar to those in Plates 25 and 26 have also been mapped with considerable precision

---

Plate 26. Vegetation and soil patterns at Thetford Heath, Suffolk (TL849795). At A *are seen alternating strips of* Calluna vulgaris (*Common ling*) *and bent-fescue grassland. The calcifuge* Calluna *is rooted in deep troughs of acid sand, while the grassland, containing less tolerant species, dominates where chalk or chalky drift comes closer to the surface. In area* B *the surface soil has been removed by recent bulldozing and the sub-surface system of sandy troughs and chalky ridges is clearly displayed. Note the prolongation of the strips of* Calluna *into the sandy troughs, and the continuation of the pattern, recorded less clearly by differential crop growth, on the other side of the road at* C.

In general, the strips lie accurately perpendicular to the contours on the O.S. 1 : 25,000 scale maps. This accord with existing slopes suggests a fairly late date for the origin of the patterns, probably during the Hunstanton (= Weichselian) Advance towards the close of the Pleistocene Ice Age. Locally, however, some strips are observed to be not quite perpendicular to the contours. Whether this deviation is due to minor inaccuracies in the printed contours, or to slight erosion since the formation of the patterns, is not yet certain.

V-AJ 13. Vertical photograph, scale 1 : 800   17 August 1961

Plates 27a and b. Soil-formation on Wash sediments ('Fen silt') at Wolferton, Norfolk (TF641299). Interpretation by D. A. MacLeod.

Since Roman times, sand, silt and clay have been continuously deposited round the margins of the Wash by incoming tides. The coarse-grained particles are deposited first to form sand-flats and banks; as the velocity of the tides decreases, finer-grained particles are laid down. When sediments have accumulated to a certain height, colonisation by marsh plants gives rise to a band of salt-marsh bordering most of the coastline of the Wash. The marsh is drained by a dendritic pattern of creeks bordered by low levees.

The stages in the development of the soil-profiles have been found broadly to correspond with the stages in development of vegetation; the main soil types can thus be mapped indirectly from air photographs. Photographs do not, however, permit unambiguous determination of all aspects of soil-profiles; for example, the depth of heavy-textured topsoil, which apparently does not directly influence the vegetation. Apart from their use in interpretation, the value of such photographs as a base map is very evident in this difficult terrain.

Comparison of the two photographs shows clearly the alterations in the creek patterns over a period of fourteen years. Note the relative instability and

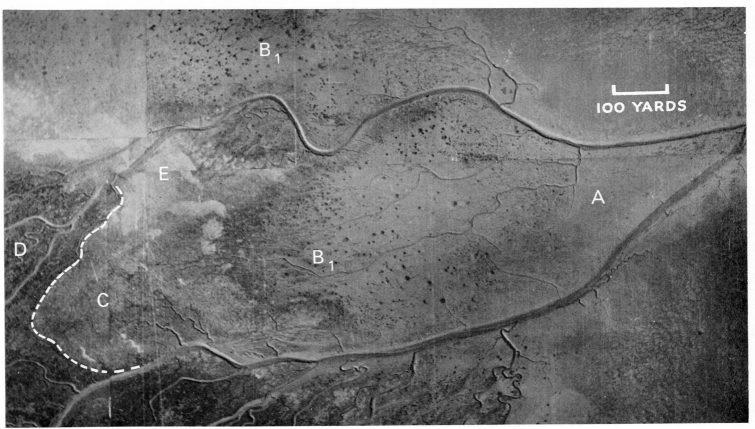

Plate 27b.   Soil formation on Wash sediments

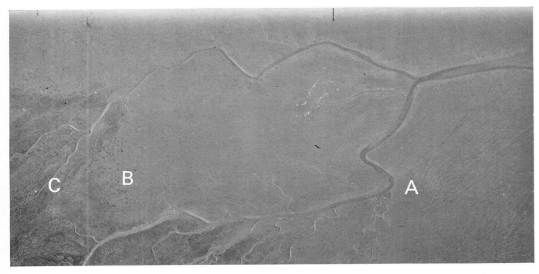

Plate 27a.   Soil formation on Wash sediments

rapid changes in the larger creeks in the bare areas low down on the marsh (A, *in both photographs*). *The smaller creeks in the upper part of the marsh are probably stabilised by the cover of vegetation* (C). *Considerable advance of the vegetation zones has occurred; for example, the zone of isolated clumps of* Spartina townsendii *which lay at* B (*Plate 27a*) *in 1946, has advanced to* B₁ (*Plate 27b*) *in 1960.*

A. *Bare deposits of silty loam or very fine sandy loam overlying sand.*

B, B₁. *Colonisation of slightly higher surfaces by isolated clumps of* Spartina townsendii.

C. *Main* Spartina *zone on silty loam thinning out towards the edges of the marsh and grading landwards into* D.

D. *Zone of* Puccinellia maritima *and* Halimione portulacoides (*sea purslane*). *This is associated with higher-lying, better-drained soils. Part of the boundary between* C *and* D *is marked on Plate 27b by a white line.*

E. *Bare ground on coarse-grained levee deposits.*

Air photography is seen to provide a simple and rapid method of assessing the rate of change of the creeks and the vegetation patterns over a period and hence of reconstructing the recent history of the marsh, a task that would be exceedingly difficult and laborious by ground survey.

(a) *R.A.F. vertical photograph 106G/UK/1427, print No. 4051.*
Scale 1 : 9,550
16 April 1946
(b) *Mosaic (prepared from R.A.F. photographs), reproduced by permission of the Sandringham Estate.   Scale 1 : 6,200*
1960

from existing vertical cover. This work was started by the author and is being completed by F. H. Nicholson.

Indirect Mapping

Normally, soils carry vegetation and cannot be mapped directly. However, the morphology of a soil is the result of the combination of *parent material* (rock or rock debris), the *age of the land surface*, the *sequence of climates* during the period of soil development, the *topography* of the site and *biotic factors*, of which vegetation and human interference are the most important. Since processes of erosion, deposition and drainage are closely related to topography, the soils in a given landscape do not occur in random array but normally in *catenas*, in which the distribution of soils is intimately linked with the relief.

In theory, if the effect of every factor were known, it would be possible to deduce the soil distribution from first principles. In fact, this knowledge is never complete. Nevertheless, topography may be measured directly from photographs in stereo-pairs and, with adequate local experience, patterns of drainage, erosion, vegetation and land-use can be identified fairly readily. It is then possible to make reasonable correlations between the soil types observed on the ground in a particular locality and the appearance of the same site on an air photograph. But it must be emphasised that the precision of a map prepared in this way will depend almost entirely on local knowledge and the experience of the interpreter and on the closeness of ground checks and controls.

The method can be applied over a range of scales but, except in specialised studies as are described in Plates 27 and 28, is unlikely to compete seriously with conventional ground survey at scales greater than 1 : 50,000. It is thus of particular value in difficult terrain or under-developed countries, where a broad inventory of natural resources is needed but where rapidity and cheapness are requirements ruling out a complete ground survey. In such cases the choice may lie between the use of air survey methods and the abandonment of the project. An important early example was the Central African Rail Link Development Survey.[5] The resulting maps, although not very precise due to restricted ground control, were able nevertheless to focus attention on those areas calling for more intensive effort. Plate 31 illustrates an area in Tanzania, where the pattern of soils can be mapped, in part directly, from tonal differences, and in part indirectly, from local knowledge of the relationships of the soil *catenas* to topography and vegetation. As a further example, in the recently completed soil survey of Uganda,[6] much of the routine mapping was performed by interpolation on air photographs between widely-spaced ground traverses. Intensive prior study of the patterns of soils in relation to topography and vegetation

(continued on page 73)

Plate 28.   Outmarsh and reclaimed land at North Wootton, Norfolk (TF605255).   Interpretation by D. A. MacLeod.

When an area of salt marsh is considered to have accumulated a sufficient depth of fine-textured silt, and to have attained a suitable height above mean sea level, the sea can be excluded by constructing a bank of material dug from the marsh sediments, a 'sock' (soak) drain being laid out alongside the line of the bank on the landward side. The enclosed creek system is then rationalised, a few of the larger creeks being retained as major drainage channels and the smaller ones filled in.

A. *Zone of* Spartina (*Cordgrass*) *with* Puccinellia (*Sea poa*) *on better-drained areas along the creeks. Note the very light tone of the* Spartina *at this season in contrast to the darker tones recorded in spring (Plate 27).*

B. *Zone dominated by* Puccinellia (*black*).

C. *Clearly defined areas (white) of* Agropyron pungens (*Sea-couch*) *developed on well-drained soils adjacent to creeks in* Puccinellia *zone.*

D. *'Sock' or soak drain, used for collecting water and for checking seepages of salt water under the bank (showing as a white line inside the bank).*

E. *Pattern of infilled creeks in reclaimed land (cf. Plate 30).*

Air photographs afford a valuable guide to the civil engineer in planning the reclamation of such marshes. The number of creeks, and even their size and depth, can be readily measured by use of photographs in stereo-pairs. This greatly helps in making a choice of larger creeks to be used as major drainage-ways, in the siting of tidal-sluices, and in the estimation of the material and the labour likely to be needed for infilling the minor creeks. Another important application arises from the ready delimitation of the relatively dry and firm Puccinellia *zone from the poorly drained sticky areas colonised by* Spartina. *The* Puccinellia *zone not only provides a surface capable of bearing heavy equipment, but also a supply of close-knit turf which can be used for stabilising the newly constructed bank.*

Study of the intricate chemical changes occurring in soils after reclamation demands samples taken from sites unaffected by former creeks. When creeks have been filled in they may be difficult to recognise on the ground, but they remain clearly visible on air photographs. Examination of the photographs is thus a valuable guide to a field-worker undertaking such sampling.

V-AT 86.   Vertical photograph; scale 1 : 3,350   5 June 1962

Plate 28. Outmarsh and reclaimed land

Plate 29. Fenland edge, Suffolk

Plate 29. Edge of the Fens, north of Mildenhall, Suffolk (TL712790). Interpretation by R. Seale, Soil Survey of England and Wales.

This photograph shows an area of well-marked hummock-and-hollow topography with a relief of up to eight feet. The hummocks are of sand supporting light, freely drained soils, while the hollows, which are poorly drained, contain peat up to 3 feet in depth yielding a humose loam topsoil.

On bare ground the sandy soils show up in light tones, and the peaty soils in dark (A). Alternatively, when photographs have been taken in conditions of lighting which emphasise the relief, the hummocks can be mapped by use of stereo-pairs of photographs. In areas carrying vegetation, more care in interpretation is needed since the pattern of tones may be reversed owing to the varying effects of drainage on differing types of vegetation. Compare for example area B, where the hummocks are recorded as dark patches, with C where they are light in tone. As in Plate 30, there is an absence of observable patterns in the higher ground at D. Here, however, the generally light soil texture may be deduced from the lines of trees, planted as wind-breaks between the cultivated fields. R.A.F. vertical photograph CPE/UK/1801, print No. 3191.   Scale 1 : 10,350   25 October 1946

Plate 30. Edge of the Cambridgeshire Fens SW. of March (TL 402951). Interpretation by R. Seale.

Area A shows a pattern of former watercourses which once traversed the estuarine clay underlying the fresh-water peat-swamps of the Fens. These watercourses were lined with calcareous alluvium, ranging in texture from fine sandy loam, in the larger courses, to clay loam in the smaller. After the draining of the Fens, wastage of the peat occurred so that the larger watercourses are now seen as banks, known as 'roddons', a name derived from the belief that they represented old roads across the marshes.

The smaller watercourses are not easy to detect on the ground except by exceedingly detailed survey, but they are readily identified and mapped on air photographs taken after fresh ploughing, when the ground is bare, by reason of the contrast in tone between the light-coloured alluvium and the dark peat. The soils cannot be mapped so easily where the ground is under crop or grass (at B), although cereal crops and certain root crops often give a vividly clear picture of such features in terms of crop marks. Note the absence of patterns in the higher ground at C. The heavy character of the soil at D can be inferred from the shapes of the fields, the drainage-ditches and the traces of medieval ridge and furrow. Fairey Air Surveys Ltd, 300024. Vertical photograph; scale 1 : 5,650   24 March 1949

Plate 30.   Fenland edge, Cambridgeshire

Plate 31. Inselbergs, pediments and 'mbuga', 20 miles NW. of Dodoma, Tanzania. Interpretation by D. A. MacLeod and R. M. S. Perrin.

Over much of the African continent, soils are developed on crystalline basement rocks, or their debris, and often occur in well defined catenas, *or recurring patterns, closely linked to the topography. The catenary concept greatly facilitates interpretation and mapping of soils from air photographs.*

In this area, the catena may be represented by a sketch. The system of lettering is the same for both sketch and photograph.

A. *Bare rock surfaces, shallow immature soils on steep slopes and deeper soils in pockets. Little vegetation except in these pockets.*

B. *Red soils (loamy sands to sandy loams), fairly shallow and freely or excessively drained. Open woodland (B_1), or savannah, but often cultivated (B_2) and then subject to erosion in varying degree.*

C. *Pale yellowish brown ('pallid') soils. Loamy sands over sandy loams containing variable amounts of concretionary iron oxides. Imperfectly drained in the wet season. Savannah or in cultivation.*

D. *Pale grey-brown medium or coarse sands over loamy sands at depth. Poorly drained in the wet season. Often practically bare of vegetation.*

E. *Dark grey or black clays. Seasonally flooded—such areas are known as 'mbugas'. Grass-covered (E_1) or bare surfaces (E_2); often fringed with* Acacia seyal, *etc. (E_3).*

The 'mbuga' shown is of unusually small size and clearly defined elongated shape. These features could be interpreted as due to recent faulting approximately parallel to the long axis of the 'mbuga'. Possibly this is a reason why the catena here extends over a much shorter distance than usual, the red soils locally coming very close to the edge of the 'mbuga'.

This interpretation is based upon careful examination of the topography as seen on photographs of good quality viewed as stereo-pairs, and could not have been carried out on single prints; nor would it have been possible without local knowledge of the interplay of the soil-forming factors.

R.A.F. vertical photograph 82A/263/TAN, print No. 5055.

Scale 1 : 27,800   *11 August 1949*

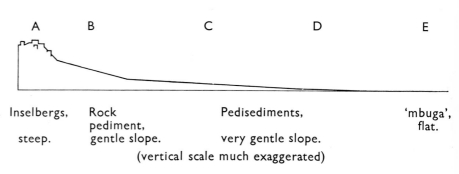

A	B	C	D	E

Inselbergs, steep.　　Rock pediment, gentle slope.　　Pedisediments, very gentle slope.　　'mbuga', flat.

(vertical scale much exaggerated)

Plate 31.   Inselbergs

allowed reasonably accurate maps to be produced very quickly in this way.

The application to large-scale mapping illustrated in Plates 27 and 28 would also be possible on vertical cover of the area shown in Plate 26. In both these cases the climate is homogeneous; the soil distribution is thus clearly reflected in the vegetation and can be fairly precisely mapped from it.

In recent years attempts have been made to devise systems whereby the soil properties in an unvisited or inaccessible area of which air photographic cover is available may be deduced by analogy with those of a well-documented region. An elementary system based on the assessment of land-use, vegetation and topography has been described for British conditions by Clarke.[7] In a wider context, a physiographic approach in which the landscape is divided into a limited number of 'facets', each of which shows reasonable homogeneity of soil properties, and which can be grouped into recurring patterns, shows some promise. Webster has successfully applied the method to the English Midlands,[8] and its applicability to hot desert regions is being tested by C. W. Mitchell.

In all these applications the requirement is again for recent vertical cover of high quality. The optimum scale will depend on the nature of the project, but photographs at 1 : 10,000 and 1 : 20,000 are the most generally useful. Because of the special importance of fine details of the topography as diagnostic features, good stereo-overlap is essential, and interpretation is greatly improved if the camera is of short focal length, for example 6 or 10 inches.

Infra-red and colour photographs sometimes considerably facilitate the identification of vegetation, and hence of soil-patterns.[9] As in direct mapping their use will certainly be extended.

NOTES

[1] American Society of Photogrammetry, *Manual of Photographic Interpretation*, (Washington, 1960), especially Chapters 5, 6 and 11.

[2] A. S. Watt, 'Stone Stripes in Breckland Norfolk', *Geol. Mag.* **92** (1955), 173-4.

[3] R. M. S. Perrin, 'Uses of Air Photographs in the Study of Patterned Ground in East Anglia', *Arch. Int. Photogrammetrie* **14** (1963), 183-8; R. B. G. Williams, 'Fossil Patterned Ground in Eastern England', *Biulletyn Peryglacjalny* **14** (1964), 337-49.

[4] Cambridge University Collection, Photo. No. F-H53, 25 June 1961: see also, R. Agache, *Bull. Soc. Prehist. Nord* **6** (1964), Figs. 97-9, Plate 30.

[5] *Report on Central African Rail Link Development Survey*, 2 vols. (Colonial Office, 1952).

[6] E. M. Chenery, *Introduction to the Soils of the Uganda Protectorate* (Dept. of Agric., Uganda, 1960).

[7] G. R. Clarke, *Study of the Soil in the Field* (Oxford, 1957).

[8] R. Webster, 'The Use of Basic Physiographic Units in Air Photo Interpretation', *Arch. Int. Photogrammetrie* **14** (1963), 143-8.

[9] G. E. Doverspike and R. C. Heller, 'The Identification of Tree Species on Large Scale Panchromatic and Colour Photographs', *Arch. Int. Photogrammetrie* **14** (1963), 233-8; von G. Hildebrandt, 'Ein Vergleich der forstlichen Interpretation panchromatischer und infrarote Luftbilder', *Arch. Int. Photogrammetrie* **14** (1963), 239-44.

Other relevant papers of interest will be found in *Arch. Int. Photogrammetrie* **14** (1963), especially 136-98.

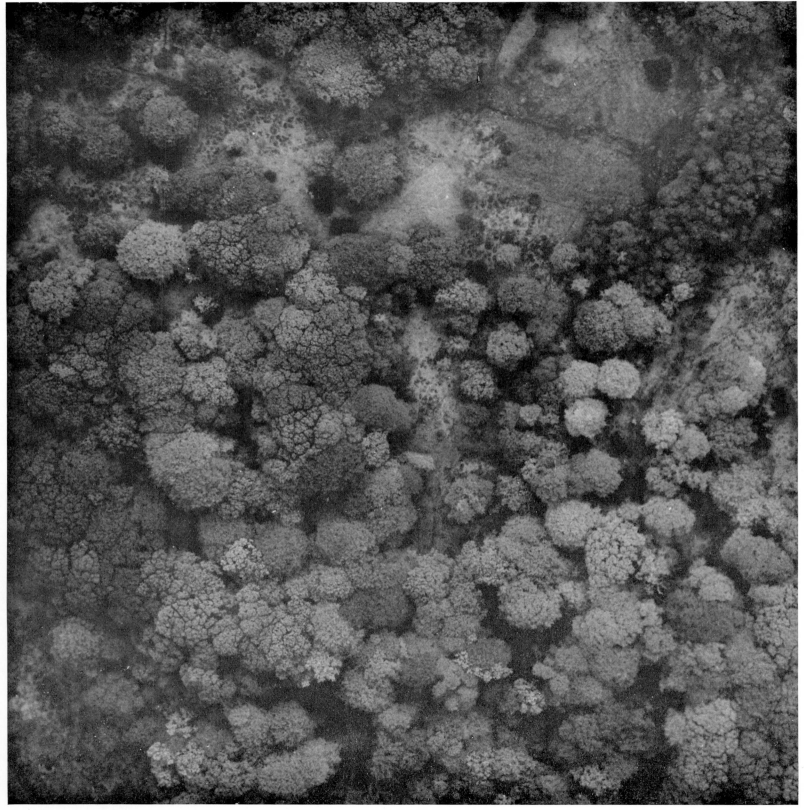

Plate 32. Bramshaw Wood (SU257155), near Romsey, in the New Forest, Hampshire. The circular canopies with fine texture are those of beech (Fagus silvatica); *the more irregular canopies, in which the clustered foliage of the separate branches is visible, are those of oak* (Quercus robur). *Much smaller black canopies of holly* (Ilex aquifolium) *are visible through gaps in the upper tree-canopies and in the glade, where a mosaic of heather bushes can also be discerned.*
V-AQ 22. Vertical photograph; scale 1 : 1,600   30 May 1962

Plate 32.   Bramshaw Wood

C. D. PIGOTT

Air Photography in Plant Ecology

THE value of air photography for recording the distribution of vegetation was recognised early in the history of air survey by Dr H. Hamshaw Thomas who emphasised this in a short paper[1] published in 1920, a few years after the end of the First World War. At about the same time, air survey was first applied to reconnaissance of forests in Canada.

Large parts of the land surfaces in temperate and tropical regions are so densely covered by vegetation that, when viewed from the air, the recognition of soils and geological features depends to a very large extent on a knowledge of their influence on vegetation. A fine example illustrated in the *Encyclopedia of Plant Physiology*[2] shows outcrops of the ultrabasic rock, serpentine, clearly demarcated in air photographs of forest in California because the vegetation it supports is sparse and stunted by comparison with that on the surrounding rocks. Such information may be of considerable and sometimes unexpected economic value; for instance, air reconnaissance has been used in Canada to locate stands of Jack Pine (*Pinus banksiana*). This tree is widespread in forest which has at some time been burnt, but in undisturbed forest this species usually occupies deposits of sandy gravel which are normally suitable for providing ballast for making concrete. Even where natural vegetation has been destroyed and replaced by crops, variations in soil conditions associated with geological features or produced artificially by cultivation are often conspicuous from the air as differences in the density, vigour and colour of the crop.

The direct value of air photography to botany lies above all in its use as an aid to the study of the distribution and structure of vegetation. Although less accurate than ground survey, the outstanding advantage of air survey is the great rapidity with which it can be accomplished. Thus, a few days may suffice to survey a large area, while to record the same amount of detail by working only on the ground would perhaps take as many years. This speed also gives air survey a special value as a method for recording transient features of vegetation, and for following the relatively fast changes which occur in the vegetation of coastal mudflats, salt marshes and sand dunes, and around the margin of freshwater lakes.

For primary survey, the value of air photographs depends on their interpretation and the accurate identification of the vegetation recorded. Identification is most satisfactorily based on a series of sample plots which can be studied both on the ground and on air photographs. In general, the ability to differentiate between vegetation types and even plant species depends on the scale of detail which can be resolved in the photograph, and this is determined by a variety of factors. Obviously the quality of photographic equipment and the altitude from which the photograph is taken are very important, but so also are variations in the conditions which control the reflection of light by vegetation, such as the amount of haze, the altitude of the sun, the amount of reflection from clouds, and whether the leaf surfaces are wet or dry. Leaves reflect the greatest proportion of incident light in the green parts of the spectrum (540–560 mμ) but they also reflect a very much higher proportion of infra-red radiation (710–1700 mμ). Film which is sensitive to infra-red records a very bright image of foliage, but to print this image in detail, the shadows become almost black because they are lit mainly by diffuse radiation from the sky which is rich in blue light.

Resolution of detail by enlargement is limited eventually by the diameter of the particles which form the grain of the film, so that small-scale features can generally be discerned only on photographs taken from a low altitude. For instance, details of foliage sufficient to allow identification even of trees with large leaves such as sycamore (*Acer pseudoplatanus*) and horse chestnut (*Aesculus hippocastanum*) can only be recognised on photographs at scales larger than $1 : 1,000$, but the contribution of the leaves and branches to the textual appearance of the tree-crown may allow species to be reliably recognised on photographs at a much smaller scale, once these features have been correlated with

(continued on page 81)

75

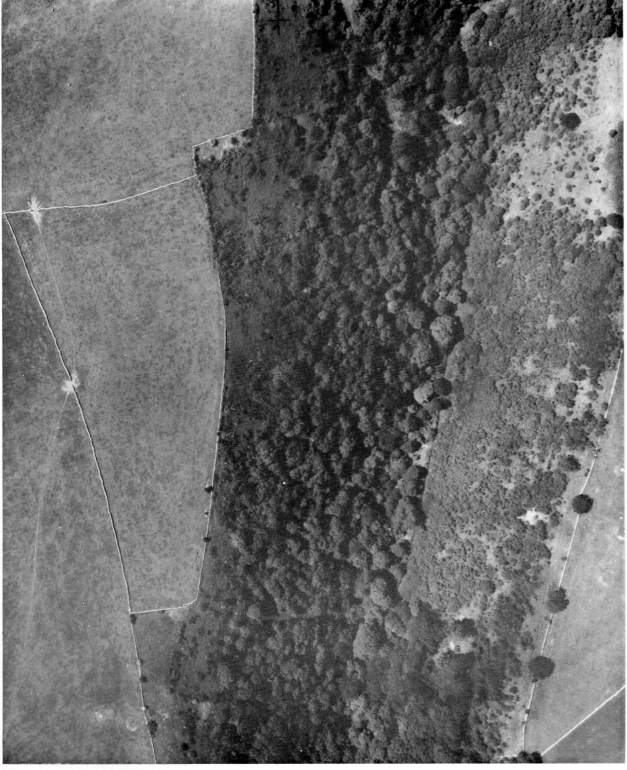

Plate 33. Lathkill Dale (SK191657), *Bakewell, Derbyshire. The north* (right-hand) *slope of this steep-sided valley in the Derbyshire limestones was formerly grazed. The old pasture is now being colonised by scrub which is largely composed of hawthorn* (Crataegus monogyna). *The wood on the south slope is composed of ash* (Fraxinus excelsior), *elm* (Ulmus glabra) *and sycamore* (Acer pseudoplatanus). (*Several large sycamores are present at the foot of the wood.*) *The uncultivated slope above the wood is densely covered by bracken* (Pteridium aquilinum) *with patches of elder* (Sambucus nigra) *on the sites of old rabbit warrens.*
V-BW 68. Vertical photograph; scale 1 : 2,150   20 July 1963

Plate 34. Tarn Moss, Malham, Yorkshire (SD888668). *This is a raised-bog which has been much modified by burning and grazing. The surface vegetation of the moss is largely composed of cotton-grass* (Eriophorum vaginatum) *and heather* (Calluna vulgaris). *The trees are small pines which were planted at the end of the nineteenth century. The stony beach of the tarn near the centre of the photograph is the top of one of the mounds of glacial moraine over which the bog has grown.*
V-AH 84. Vertical photograph; scale 1 : 1,250   22 July 1961

Plate 33.   Lathkill Dale

Plate 34.   Tarn Moss, Malham

Plate 35.   Colt Park Wood

Plate 35. Colt Park Wood, Ribblesdale, Yorkshire (SD775771). Scattered ash trees occupy the fissured surface of an outcrop of limestone. Most of the grassland is on shallow soils which are developed from glacial drift overlying the limestone. In the area bounded by the sinuous stone wall above (to left of) the wood, the drift is deep enough to support bracken.
V–AH 65.   Vertical photograph; scale 1 : 1,250
22 July 1961

Plate 36. Silver Flowe, Kirkcudbrightshire (NX471843). An oblique view of a large raised-bog showing the concentric arrangement of pools either as open water or filled with floating Sphagnum. *Between the pools can be seen hummocks of* Sphagnum *typical of an actively growing peat bog.*
UV 24   30 May 1957

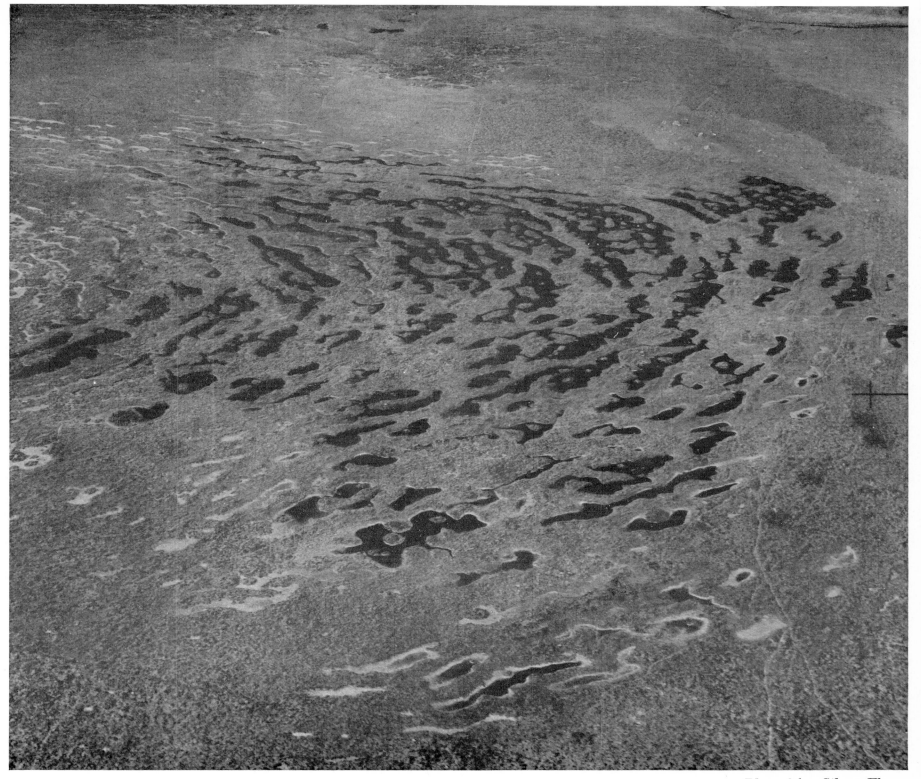

Plate 36. Silver Flowe

Plate 37. Abbots Moss, Cheshire (SJ601687). Floating mats of reed (Phragmites communis) and reedmace (Typha sp.) fringe the open water and support scattered bushes and thickets of willow.
V–BY 16. Vertical photograph; scale 1 : 1,950
20 July 1963

Plate 37.   Abbots Moss

specimens identified on the ground. In the photograph of part of Bramshaw wood in the New Forest (Plate 32), the crowns of beech (*Fagus silvatica*) are darker grey and finer textured than the crowns of oak (*Quercus robur*), in which the leaves are clustered so that the separate branches are more or less distinct. The canopies of holly (*Ilex aquifolium*) appear black and show no detail. Comparable differences between ash (*Fraxinus excelsior*), elm (*Ulmus glabra*) and sycamore are illustrated in the photograph of Lathkill Dale in Derbyshire (Plate 33). Trees are, of course, relatively large objects and the crowns of deciduous forest-trees are still individually separate at scales approaching 1 : 90,000, though the distinctive features of crown shape and texture which enable species to be identified are lost at scales smaller than 1 : 25,000. Advantage can often be taken of differences in the time of leaf unfolding and leaf fall as an aid to identification, and in primary survey, oblique photographs, because they provide a more familiar view of trees, may assist in identifying species on corresponding vertical cover. Plants very much smaller than trees are also individually visible on aerial photographs at scales greater than 1 : 15,000. The photograph of Tarn Moss at Malham in Yorkshire (Plate 34) shows in detail the distribution of individual bushes of heather (*Calluna vulgaris*) and on the original print the tussocks of cotton-grass (*Eriophorum vaginatum*) are also visible.

As well as their use in primary survey of vegetation, air photographs can be of very great assistance in ground survey. They are probably most conveniently used in conjunction with large-scale maps, and they then provide a rapid method of locating the exact position of sites on the ground. This also offers a simple method for obtaining a randomised distribution of sample sites for vegetation or soil analyses. A grid is superimposed on to the photograph and sites are selected by using a table of random numbers to provide a series of co-ordinates.

Low-altitude photographs may be used in the investigation of the structure of vegetation as a basis for quantitative studies of the density and area occupied by individual species. In the photographs of the New Forest and of Lathkill Dale, it is a relatively simple task to map the canopies of the individual trees and count the numbers of trees in sample areas. Charting of tree canopies by an observer on the forest floor is slow and difficult. It is also possible to measure the heights of trees on photographs, either from measurements of their shadows on level ground, or by measurements of parallax. Trunk girth is sufficiently closely correlated with crown diameter in particular species for it to be possible to make useful estimates of timber volumes. Not uncommonly structural features of vegetation are conspicuous from the air which would be overlooked by an observer on the ground. An interesting example is provided by the sand dunes at Holkham on the coast of Norfolk. In aerial views of this and many other dune systems it is at once obvious that much of the bare sand is related to an intricate network of footpaths. Few ecologists appreciate how much of the bare sand in some dune systems is the product of human interference. Another example may be seen in the photograph of Colt Park Wood on the slope of Ingleborough in Yorkshire (Plate 35). This view shows ash trees scattered over an outcrop of limestone, and in the pasture above the wood it is clear that the limestone wall exactly coincides with the edge of an area of glacial drift, sufficiently deep to support a dense growth of bracken. It seems unlikely that the wall was built along the edge but rather that drift has been either lost from the area outside the wall, or even added to the area enclosed. Evidence of former ploughing is often visible on air photographs in sites where it would almost certainly be overlooked by observation on the ground. In the original print of the photograph of Lathkill Dale, a regular pattern of plough furrows can be discerned in the pastures above the wooded slope but in this case their presence had not been noticed during a detailed study of the composition of the grassland.

Air survey has a special advantage for studying the structure of vegetation which would be damaged and modified by ground survey. Marshes, fens and bogs are particularly vulnerable in this way and it would be impossible to map the distribution of a complex pattern of pools and hummocks of *Sphagnum* as shown in the photographs of Silver Flowe in Kirkcudbrightshire (Plate 36), without transecting at closely spaced intervals and causing extensive damage by treading down the spongy surface. Moreover, this type of vegetation may be almost inaccessible on foot and the surface is usually so unstable that instruments cannot be used accurately. The beds of reeds and reed-mace, and even the thickets of willow, which fringe many of the Cheshire and Shropshire meres (Plate 37) are in fact floating and slowly sink under the weight of a man, but the vegetation zones can be mapped with accuracy from an air photograph.

NOTES

[1] Thomas, H. H., 'Aircraft photography in the service of science', *Nature* **105** (1920), 457–9.

[2] Krause, W., 'Andere Boden spezialisten', *Encyclopedia of Plant Physiology* **4** (Berlin, 1958), 789.

J. RISHBETH

Applications of Air Photography to Problems of Plant Disease

AS fields are enlarged in response to the greater mechanisation of agriculture there is increasing difficulty in recording the extent and severity of crop diseases, and sometimes these are not even detected before harvest. Again, as the world demand for timber increases, felling is intensified in accessible areas and is extended to forests formerly inaccessible: as a result certain types of tree disease, for which traditional methods of survey and assessment are inadequate, are becoming more prevalent. In these circumstances it is scarcely surprising that plant pathologists have considered in what ways air photography might be applied to some of their problems.

The first recorded attempts to photograph from the air the effects of plant disease were made in Texas in 1927. It had proved most difficult to obtain from the ground satisfactory photographs of cotton root rot, caused by the fungus *Phymatotrichum omnivorum*, and a series of oblique photographs were taken from altitudes of 250 to 500 feet with panchromatic film and a light yellow filter. These showed fields where healthy cotton plants formed a continuous ground cover, dark in tone, with groups which had already wilted or died exposing the light-toned soil. In the subsequent report it was suggested that the method might be valuable for estimating losses as well as for obtaining better photographs of field experiments.[1]

Some twenty-five years elapsed before air photography was used again for such purposes. By this time the principles determining reflection and absorption of light by vegetation were better understood, and in 1952 Colwell expressed the view that it should be possible to predict the air-photographic tone or colour of an object for any particular combination of film and filter. Subsequent extensive research on experimental plots of various cereals in California showed how closely this prediction was realised.[2] Some of the main findings may be illustrated by results obtained from oats infected by the rust fungus *Puccinia graminis*. Light from the blue and red portions of the spectrum is largely absorbed by the pigment in healthy leaves, only about 10 per cent of these portions of incident sunlight being reflected to the camera, whereas some 20 per cent of the green portion is reflected. By contrast at least 80 per cent in the infra-red part of the spectrum is reflected, so

(continued on page 88)

Plate 38. The use of infra-red film to record plant disease. An initial infection-centre of potato blight (A) in a field of the variety 'Red King' near Lakenheath, Suffolk (TL712790), appears on the photograph as an area of darker tone, contrasting with the healthy (light-toned) plants elsewhere. Secondary infection-centres have developed nearby (B) in a field of the same variety. Still further spread of the disease has occurred from these secondary patches, giving them a blurred appearance.
Vertical photograph; scale 1 : 3,750   *16 July 1960*

Plate 39. Twenty-five-year-old Scots pines on former arable land at Breckles Heath, Norfolk (TL920940). The operations of thinning and rack-cutting (removal of two rows for access) carried out eight years earlier, led to the development of root disease around stumps infected by the fungus Fomes annosus. Small disease gaps are not easily seen at this angle, but a larger gap (1) originating from an infected thinning stump, and a roughly semi-circular one (2), developing from one or more infected rack stumps, are clearly visible.
QG 42   *28 June 1955*

Plate 38. Infection-centres of potato blight

Plate 39. Scots pines

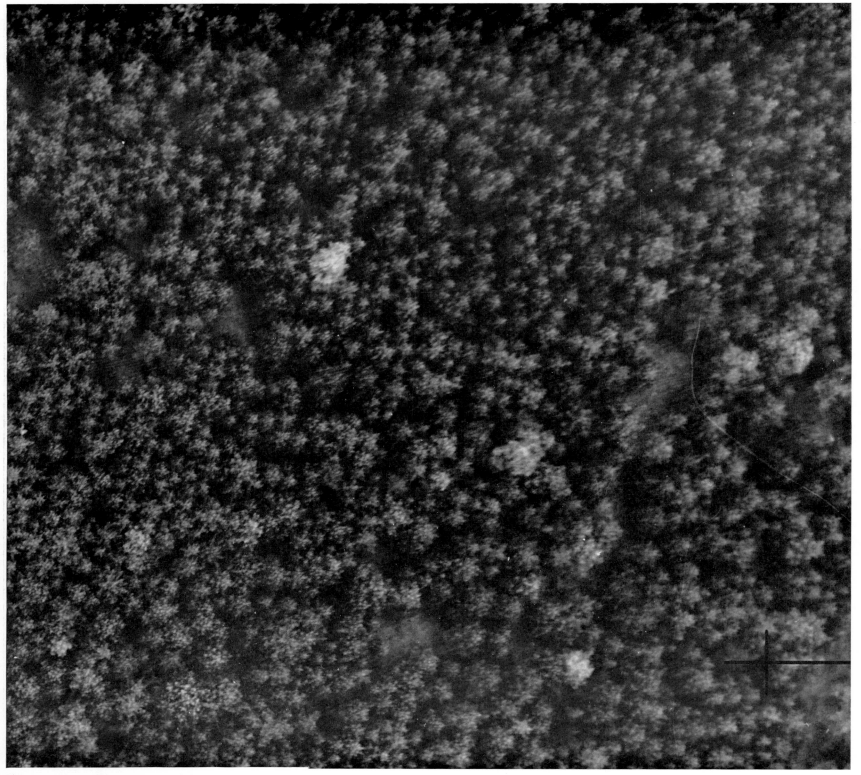

Plates 40a and b. Different sections, 400 yards apart, of the same replanted area near Croxton, Norfolk (approximate centre TL853882), taken on a dull day in July 1961, when the virtual absence of shadow allowed a clear picture of the extent to which the tree canopy had been affected. Twenty-one-year-old Corsican pines are growing on the site of a young plantation destroyed by fire, where many small stumps became infected by Fomes annosus. *Where the soil is acidic (a) earlier scattered killing has almost ceased and only small gaps occur, as may be judged by the almost uniform tone of the photograph. The few larger, light-toned trees are hardwoods such as birch. Where the soil is alkaline, (b) root disease is much more severe, the irregular light areas representing grassy patches where all the trees have died. Moreover, the disease is still advancing, as indicated by the lighter-toned trees around the edges of gaps; these represent pines in various stages of attack.*
V-AE 75 and 76. Vertical photographs; scale 1 : 250   14 July 1961

Plate 40a.   Plantation of Corsican pines

Plate 40b.   Plantation of Corsican pines

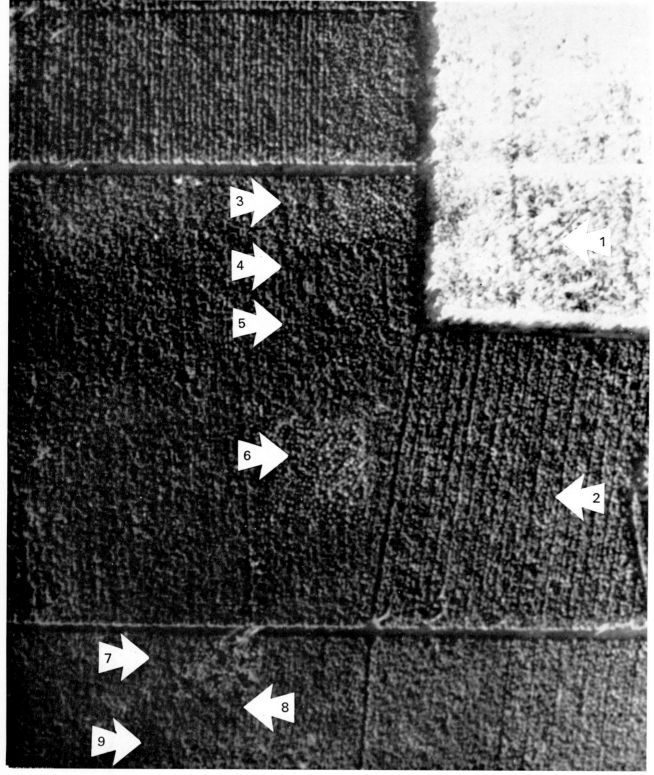

Plate 41a. Wangford Warren, Suffolk (TL767820). Seven-year-old Scots pines (SP) on former woodland and twenty-year-old Scots pines and Corsican pines (CP) on former grassland, the soil in each case being alkaline. In the younger Scots pines (1) the irregular light patches represent grass: fully a quarter of the trees have already been killed by Fomes annosus. *A portion of the older Corsican crop (2) had been thinned the previous year by removing whole rows at regular intervals. Much of the remaining area was taken up by a thinning experiment in which different proportions of trees were removed four years before the photograph was taken. The various plots are shown as follows: heavily thinned CP (3); unthinned CP (4); lightly thinned CP (5); very heavily thinned CP (6); very heavily thinned SP (7), which already shows disease gaps; unthinned SP (8); lightly thinned SP (9). R.A.F. vertical photograph 3G/TUD/UK 59 Part IV, print No. 5400.*

Scale 1 : 4,140　　　　　　　　　　　　　　　　*5 February 1946*

Plate 41a.   Scots pines and Corsican pines, 1946

Plate 41b. The same area of Wangford Warren nine years later. The Scots pines on former woodland (1) show irregular gaps due to Fomes *attack, but much of the canopy is beginning to close. In the line-thinned Corsican pines (2) little disease is apparent because very few of the stumps became infected with* Fomes. *No attack has developed in the unthinned plots (4, 8). Trees have been killed in all the thinned plots (3, 5, 6, 7, 9), following stump infection by* Fomes, *attacks being somewhat heavier in the more susceptible Scots pines.*
PC 55   *19 March 1955*

Plate 41b. Scots pines and Corsican pines, 1955

that a young healthy oat crop appears light in tone when photographed with infra-red film in combination with a deep red filter to eliminate the visible portion of the spectrum.

The amount of infra-red radiation reflected from oat leaves was found to decline very soon after plants became diseased, probably because the fungus invades internal leaf spaces. Thus while such plants were still normally green in appearance and no tone difference was detectable with panchromatic film, they appeared dark-toned with infra-red film as compared with light-toned healthy plants. Two or three weeks elapsed before reflection of orange and red light increased sufficiently to enable detection by panchromatic film. Not only did infra-red film allow earlier detection, but there was little reduction in tone-contrast between diseased and healthy plants photographed from progressively greater altitudes up to 10,000 feet; with panchromatic film such reduction commonly occurred through scattering of light by atmospheric haze. However panchromatic or colour photographs were commonly superior for illustrating later stages of disease because even healthy plants lose much of their ability to reflect infra-red radiation as they approach maturity.

The two features of infra-red air photography mentioned above are potentially important for the attempted control of cereal diseases. Cereal crops are often severely damaged by diseases: for instance losses as high as 75 per cent due to killing by rust have been recorded for some wheats in the United States. Under certain conditions early detection and treatment of infection-centres might permit economic control of a disease before serious losses occur. Ability to detect disease from a considerable altitude is important where complete coverage is required for large areas: for such purposes low-altitude photography is considered uneconomic. It is well to realise that disease assessment of field crops from the air by means of infra-red photography can never be entirely reliable because, for example, patches of bare ground or flooded areas also appear dark in tone and may be mistaken for diseased plants. However, the method can at least eliminate from further ground-study obviously healthy crops occupying, in most instances, the greater part of the surveyed area.

An interesting application of air photography to another field-crop, potatoes, has recently been made in Britain by Brenchley and Dadd.[3] Potato blight, caused by the fungus *Phytophthora infestans*, is a common disease which varies greatly in severity with district and season, largely according to weather conditions. Little is known about the way in which blight epidemics build up, and in particular there is virtually no information about the number and distribution of early disease-patches or foci from which many epidemics develop. Air photographs have revealed early stages to an extent virtually impossible to attain on the ground, so large are the areas to be surveyed. Once again, for this predominantly leaf-infecting parasite, infra-red photography was employed to detect early stages.

One such photograph (Plate 38) reproduced here shows an initial focus first reported in early July 1960, near Lakenheath in Suffolk. When this patch was photographed from the air twelve days later its diameter had greatly increased and some fifty new patches were discernible in a potato field lying to the north. From existing knowledge of the disease it seemed certain that these were all derived from the original focus through dispersal of air-borne *Phytophthora* spores. Moreover, since such spread occurs only under well-defined conditions of temperature and humidity, the actual day on which it occurred could be determined with a fair degree of certainty from weather records. The photograph also provides evidence of spread from the new patches, which are characterised by a blurred extension to the south-west. These represent plants at earlier stages of disease which were probably infected when conditions again favoured spore dispersal and the wind was north-easterly. Air photography thus revealed a pattern of blight development which probably would not have been noticed from the ground, and it seems likely that the method can be more generally applied for studying the ways in which certain diseases develop in field crops.

It is less certain whether air photography will materially assist control of diseases such as potato blight. In parts of Britain where the weather is known to favour epidemics, spraying or dusting of potatoes with a suitable copper preparation is a routine procedure and early detection of the disease is of no special advantage. By contrast, in many other areas detection of primary infection foci is potentially important in about one year out of five, when the weather favours severe blight, but not in the other four years when blight is less serious and spraying is considered uneconomic.

One use of air photographs suggested earlier, that of illustrating field experiments, is now increasingly recognised. A good example is provided by work in Central America on banana wilt, caused by the fungus *Fusarium oxysporum f. cubense*.[4] Bananas, though technically a herbaceous crop, are often so tall and crowded that adequate photographs are seldom obtainable from the ground, but in this instance an oblique air photograph of an experiment testing the virulence of various strains of the fungus clearly shows how destructive one was by

Plate 42. The same area of Wangford Warren taken 16 years after Plate 41a. The Scots pines on former woodland (1) show almost complete closure of the canopy despite the initial heavy Fomes *attack. The line-thinned Corsican pines (2) are still healthy. Surviving Corsican pines in one of the thinned plots (3) are closing all but the largest gaps in the canopy. There is no disease in the unthinned Corsican pines (4); the tops are small and crowded.*

V-BA 14. Vertical photograph; scale 1 : c. 800
28 June 1962

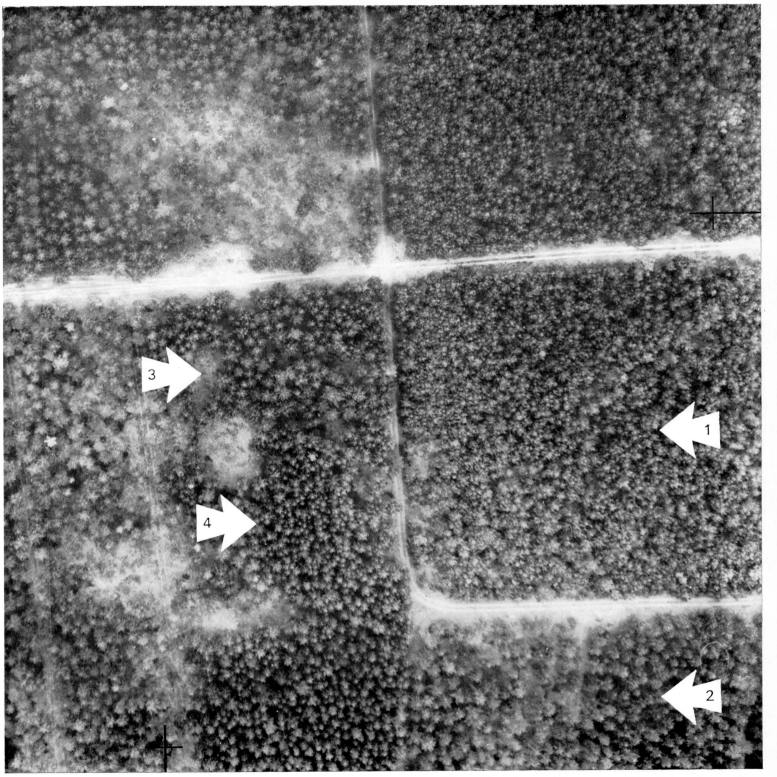

Plate 42. Scots pines and Corsican pines, 1962

comparison with others. When field-trials are carried out year after year in a limited area, as often happens in the vicinity of research stations, low-level vertical photographs can provide a valuable record of the lay-out. Sometimes, in addition, such photographs help to explain anomalous results, caused for instance by local variations in soil texture or fertility, and they may facilitate planning of future trials, for example by directing attention to sites showing recurrent crop failure. This type of application is potentially very wide and by no means confined to work on plant diseases.

Many of the points in favour of photographing field crops from the air apply with equal or even greater force to forest stands. Here again, although air reconnaissance was early employed for general surveys, it has been applied specifically to forest diseases only in the last fifteen years or so. A minor exception to this is provided, for example, by Napper who used a low-level oblique photograph to illustrate a disease gap in a Malayan rubber plantation.[5] Fowler has described surveys in the United States for oak-wilt,[6] caused by the fungus *Ceratocystis faga-cearum*, and pole blight of western white pine, a non-infectious disease. The main objects were to detect the diseases and to estimate their severity, photography being subsidiary, but the technique seems of sufficient interest to mention here. The urgency for studying oak-wilt arose from its rapid spread into surrounding States from initial outbreaks in Wisconsin, probably as a result of transmission by bark-feeding beetles: it was of great potential danger in view of the fact that oaks produce one-third of the hardwood 'saw-logs' in the United States and are most important as shade trees and ground cover. The survey was carried out mainly in Arkansas and southern Missouri, the flat terrain allowing a grid-type of flight pattern over large areas. Reconnaissance was carried out in slow-flying aircraft 200 to 500 feet above the tree-tops, enabling the observer to distinguish between the bronzed foliage of recently wilted oaks and the green crowns of surrounding healthy trees. By this means one observer could survey about 18 square miles of forest per hour; areas that had no wilted trees were eliminated from further study and ground crews were sent only into areas where disease symptoms had been seen.

More recently True and others have described similar surveys in West Virginia where the mountainous country necessitated contour-flying of watersheds.[7] They point out that several surveys each season may be required to locate new centres of infection, so rapidly do symptoms develop, and that the effectiveness of the method is reduced where many oaks have died from other causes. However, it has proved possible in some areas to locate infection-centres in the absence of leaf symptoms merely by plotting the position of groups of dead oaks from the air; this grouping results from tree-to-tree spread of the fungus through natural root grafts. Early detection of oak-wilt, greatly assisted by air reconnaissance, is essential for its control. Untreated trees not only infect any adjacent ones through their roots but they soon develop growths of the fungus under the bark, causing it to split: this allows access of insects, including the beetles which transmit the fungal parasite. Prompt felling or girdling of the infected tree, to bring about rapid dessication, is the most effective treatment.

In Britain air photography with panchromatic film has provided a useful supplementary technique for studying a root disease of pines caused by the wood-rotting fungus *Fomes annosus*. Infections occur chiefly from stumps, the fungus passing from stump roots to roots of living trees where these are in contact, and this may cause progressive killing around the original infection-centre.[8] Pines planted on sites formerly bearing conifers are often attacked almost at once, since infected stumps are already present, and where soil conditions favour development of the disease a third or more of the trees may be killed within ten years. By contrast, in plantations on former heath or arable, where at first no sources of infection exist, pines are chiefly attacked after twenty years or more. This latter type of attack arises mainly through the operations of rack-cutting, in which two rows of trees are removed to allow access, and thinning: the stumps so produced are often colonised by airborne spores of *Fomes annosus*. Subsequent progress of the fungus mainly depends on local conditions. In East Anglia serious attacks have developed in plantations on light, sandy sites especially where the soil reaction is alkaline: here the number of deaths often increases steadily from the time of the second thinning onwards. By the time the trees are about thirty years old, the average loss in yield of timber is 12 per cent and in some plantations over a quarter of the trees are killed or seriously affected.

In 1946, when this type of attack had only recently developed, air photographs taken from 10,000 feet revealed openings of the tree canopy in many places where root disease had not been reported. A ground survey showed that the majority were in fact new infection-centres, but these were not always distinguishable on the photographs from openings due to other causes. In a relatively small and accessible forest area such as this, detection of the disease by means of air photographs no longer has any advantage over ground surveys, but in vast areas of pines, as for example in the southern United States where new outbreaks are developing fast, it could be of considerable assistance.

As with other diseases already mentioned, the characteristic appearance of attacks may often be illustrated better by photography from the air than from the ground (Plate 39). Vertical photographs are specially useful for recording the extent to which the disease has created openings in the tree canopy, an assessment very difficult to make in any other way. Pines re-planted on the site of a young stand destroyed by fire, after which many small stumps became infected by *Fomes*, are shown in Plate 40. Where the soil is acidic (Plate 40a) earlier scattered killing has occurred but the disease has become stabilised and only small gaps are now visible; where it is alkaline (Plate 40b) killing still continues and some of the original gaps have coalesced. Since *Fomes* spreads relatively slowly, often at about 2 feet a year in East Anglia, air photographs may be used to record the disease over a period of years. Three stages of development are shown in Plates 41a,b and 42: in the younger pine plantation on ground formerly bearing conifers, attacks were early and severe but then diminished, whereas in the older stands on former grassland they occurred only after thinning and continued longer. With this disease immediate felling of infected trees does not prevent further attack: control is mainly directed towards preventing entry of *Fomes* into stumps, this being achieved by treating the freshly cut surface with a chemical protectant or with a fungal competitor. For extensive areas of pines, early detection of the disease by air photography might well allow, for any future thinnings, the institution of control measures if these seemed economically justifiable.

The potential uses of air photography in plant pathology may be summarised as follows. Especially where large areas are involved, the technique may usefully supplement ground surveys for detection, though it can seldom replace them. It offers excellent opportunities for illustrating and recording disease outbreaks, whether in field experiments, commercial crops or natural vegetation; and with experience losses can be estimated. Records of disease development may be obtained by photographing selected areas at appropriate intervals, and patterns of distribution may be revealed which are not evident on the ground: such information can materially aid the understanding of factors controlling disease. No general statement can be made about its application to treatment of disease because the type of control measure varies so greatly with the crop and with local conditions, and because ultimately economic factors are decisive. However, with some diseases the possibility of effective control is greatly increased by the early detection which air photography allows.

NOTES

[1] J. J. Taubenhaus, W. N. Ezekiel and C. B. Neblette, 'Airplane photography in the study of cotton root rot', *Phytopath.* **19** (1929), 1025-9.

[2] R. N. Colwell, 'Determining the prevalence of certain cereal crop diseases by means of aerial photography', *Hilgardia* **26** (1956), 223-86.

[3] G. H. Brenchley and C. V. Dadd, 'Potato blight recording by aerial photography', *N.A.A.S. Quart. Rev.* **57** (1962), 21-4.

[4] R. H. Stover, 'Studies on *Fusarium* wilt of bananas, IV', *Canad. J. Bot.* **37** (1959), 245-55.

[5] R. P. N. Napper, 'Observations on the root disease of rubber trees caused by *Fomes lignosus*', *Rep. Rubb. Res. Inst. Malaya*, 1939 (1940), 157-71.

[6] M. E. Fowler, 'Surveys for oak wilt,' *Plant Dis. Reptr.* **35** (1951), 112-18; 'Aircraft scouting for pole blight and oak wilt,' *J. For.* **50** (1952), 191-5.

[7] R. P. True, H. L. Barnett, C. K. Dorsey, and J. G. Leach, 'Oak wilt in West Virginia', *W. Va. Univ. Agr. Expt. Sta. Bull.*, 1960, 448T.

[8] J. Rishbeth, 'Observations on the biology of *Fomes annosus*, with particular reference to East Anglian pine plantations, I', *Ann. Bot. Lond.* **14** (1950), 365-83.

JOHN MILTON and
F. FRASER DARLING

Air Photography in Zoological Studies

FOR the field naturalist one of the outstanding advances of the last quarter-century has been the use of air reconnaissance for ecological research. Given the right method of approach and the necessary skill in interpretation of the results, the use of aircraft makes possible the accurate study of migrations even of large and fast-moving animals in remote and difficult terrain, with immense saving of time to the trained scientist. Nevertheless, air reconnaissance and photography does not remove the need for much hard work on the ground. An aircraft can guide, select, and broaden the view, or possibly even solve a problem at a glance, but it should never stop the biologist from examining at first hand the results obtained by this exciting new method of research.

One of the earliest uses of aircraft and later of air photography was the census of mammals, birds and even fish, in a wide variety of habitats. The species which have been studied in this way include pronghorn antelope, beaver, caribou (Plate 45), moose or elk, deer, mountain antelope or goat, musk ox, bighorn sheep, wildebeeste (Plate 50), topi, oryx, lechure, giraffe, Grant's gazelle, zebra, elephant (Plate 44), wolf, northern fur seal, walrus, harp seal (Plate 46), hooded seal, grey seal, ostrich, grouse, gannet, geese and ducks of several kinds, flamingo, bald eagle, oystercatcher (Plate 47), and salmon.

Not all such census work has been successful and accurate. Attempts to count grey seals and red deer in the difficult light of the Scottish autumn were most disappointing. The coat-pattern of the seals against wet rock and stony ground made them extremely difficult to pick out,

though improvement in photographic method will doubtless set this right in the future, and the deer were practically invisible against the sombre terrain of heather, sedge and dark rock. In contrast, the pattern of herds of zebra in the brilliant light of Africa produces a dazzling effect that makes them difficult to count except by vertical photography. Wildebeeste, on the other hand, are easy to count either directly or from photographs (Plate 50), as each dark animal has a lighter patch on the back which serves the observer like a lamp.

Leedy in an article on air photography and interpretation identified a number of potential values for wild life management:

Maps; evaluation and determination of game range; censusing game animals; locating refuge-sites; law enforcement; studying areas damaged by fire, floods, insects or disease; determining hunting pressure; locating, mapping and planning potential dam sites; plotting land-use and wild-life problem areas; determining changes in vegetative cover and land-use over a period of years; planning the locations of roads, trails, fire lanes, and other developmental features of newly acquired areas; making special studies of rare or

Plate 43. Tsavo National Park, south-east Kenya. Part of a typical breeding herd of buffalo (Syncerus caffer) *that has been disturbed by the aircraft. The extensive tree damage, attributed to the high elephant population, is a serious problem for the Kenya National Parks administration.*

Plate 43.　Breeding herd of buffalo

vanishing species in which permanent records of habitat types are desirable; conducting lake surveys, including the mapping of emergent and floating aquatic flora, and possibly the contour mapping of lake bottoms; plotting tax-delinquent lands in connection with acquisition of land for game refuge and management areas; and recording pictorially the features of breeding grounds newly discovered in remote areas.[20]

Our view is that though more use of air photography has been made for census work than in other fields of animal ecology there is still a great deal to do. There are many potentially suitable species for which a census by air photography has never been attempted, and there is room for a manual on method. Aircraft have been particularly useful for the census of massed aggregations, where photographs could be checked at leisure. For example, Spinner found that when fifty-two ornithologists looked at an air photograph of 13,494 greater snow geese in Delaware Bay,[27] individual estimates ranged from 3,000 to 28,000 birds, with an average around 9,000. When comparisons of two other pictures of the same flock were made, one showing the geese rising from their feeding grounds and the other showing the same flock settled in a compact group on the water, observers overestimated the population in the first photograph and underestimated the count in the second. Although air photographs are often a useful tool for such census work (Plate 47), the task of counting may prove tedious and even yield inexact results.

In an unpublished report to the Conservation Foundation in the spring of 1950 Per Host reported on aerial studies of the seal herds off Newfoundland.[16] Earlier work by Mr Host had indicated that hooded seals were in particular danger of extinction.

The air survey, with Dean Fisher in charge, was made between 4 and 10 March 1950, using a DC-3 aircraft, under the aegis of the Canadian Fisheries Department. As a result of his observations and photographs from the air, Mr Host concluded that the herd of harp seals did not seem to be in any immediate danger (cf. Plate 46). On the other hand, the hooded seal appeared to be in serious trouble off Newfoundland. On a basis of observations from the air and of hunting statistics Host recommended the establishment of a closed season for the latter species.

The California Division of Fish and Game has also used air photographs for wild-life inventories. William P. Dasmann, a Game Range Technician with the Bureau of Game Conservation, has stated:

In game inventories herds of animals or flocks of birds are photographed from the air, usually with a (Fairchild) K-20 camera. The prints are enlarged, and the game species counted on the picture, sometimes with the help of magnifying glasses. Sometimes counts are randomised by blocks on photos where the individuals are numerous, viz., waterfowl.

He went on to mention the value of using such photographs as maps 'to determine both topography, cultural features, and vegetation types'; Indeed, one great advantage of the technique is the ease with which wild-life habitat can be determined. Zoological studies should include detailed analyses of all habitat components.

Other chapters in this book emphasise the importance of air photography in the mapping of vegetation, soils, and geology, and here it need only be stated that the value of air photography for the mapping of vegetation is, for example, often just as important to the study of animal ecology as the census of the wild life itself.

Norman Carls has listed three advantages that an air photograph has over a map:

It has a wealth of detail no map can equal. It is reliable. Floods and other features, as they existed at the time the photograph was taken, are shown in their true relationships to one another. Usually it is more up to date than the best map available.

All of these advantages hold for the use of air photographs in the mapping of wild-life habitat; Schultz, however, enumerated two major disadvantages:

The relatively high cost of reproducing, in quantities, a finished map containing the details available on air photographs, and the large number of individual air photographs needed for coverage of an extensive area (which prohibits their direct use on a 'practical' mosaic.)[25]

In their paper on 'The use of Aerial Photographs and Ecological Principles in Cover Type Mapping', Wilson and Berard noted that

Plate 44.   Kenya National Park; small group of elephants (Loxodonta africana) *comprising four adults and six young. A photographic survey by the Army Air Corps for a census of elephants in 1963 yielded a total of 15,000 head, as against the highest estimate of 10,000.*

Plate 44.   Small group of elephants

many wild life biologists are unaware of the extent to which ecological principles can be applied in the interpretation of aerial photographs. . . . Acquired knowledge and technique in the use of photographic interpretation, comparable to the development of mapping in the field of forestry, does not yet exist in wild life management.[28]

The North-Eastern Forest Experiment Station (1949) has developed extensive type-mapping of forest cover to a high degree, particularly by relating the distribution of forest types to topography. Throughout their work, foresters have shown increasing technical ability in the classification of 'cover types' which lead to elucidation of ecological factors involved.

Particularly strong emphasis has been given to the identification of tree species by the recognition of seasonal differences. The identification of plants used by wild life for cover is most easily made in the temperate zone during the autumn.[24] Moreover, at other times of the year, patterns of vegetation marking water-courses, differing soil types, the incidence of fire, etc., can be quickly mapped with the help of air photography. A research worker armed with detailed photographs of the plant-communities in any area has his task of mapping boundaries of wild-life cover types made considerably easier. Even though the identification of many plant species may not be possible from air photographs, at least the dominant members of the various plant-communities can usually be picked out, not to mention 'indicator species'. With this information, identification of plants on the ground is greatly facilitated; and if sample plots are carefully selected in the major communities recognisable on air photographs, the detailed information obtained can often be applied more generally in interpreting the photographs for the purpose of mapping.

With the definition of these methods in plant ecology it is but a short step to relating wild life to its habitat through air photography (Plate 43). To be of value in animal ecology, however, such air surveys of plant communities are often correlated with observations of migration, distribution, dispersion, food-habits, etc. Many of these supporting studies can also be carried out from the air, but in the majority of cases a great deal of basic ground-observation is still necessary.

One of the greatest problems in biology has been the determination of migratory patterns in birds, fishes, mammals, and insects. Much of the information that has been accumulated to date has come to hand through the collection of dates and routes of migrations. Griffin and Hock have discussed the ability of birds to perceive environmental clues as a guide to direction. The authors' hypothesis was that many bird species have a well-developed topographical memory, 'so that having flown over an area in migration or in natural wanderings they can thereafter orient themselves within that familiar territory by means of landmarks'.[14]

In order to test this idea the authors released a number of gannets (*Morus basanus*) 213 miles inland from their nests, and followed their return journey by aerial observation. The results indicated that 'homing from unknown territory may involve extensive exploratory flights which for a time take the birds away from home rather than towards it'. Thus the hypothesis that 'birds' (specifically the gannet) find their way home through the use of familiar landmarks was strengthened, since the artificially transported individuals invariably explored a wide area, often heading in incorrect directions, until they reached familiar landmarks. Although no photographs were taken, the study is of particular interest in showing how important observations from the air *can* be in migrational studies. Similar values were derived by Banfield in his investigations of barren-ground caribou in Canada.[3] He used air photographs to determine the migration-habits and range of *Rangifer arcticus*, as well as data on numbers, sex, and age. Clearly, however, the potential value of air photography and observation in work on migration has only been partially realised. In future studies of migration all aspects of the record presented on air photographs should be fully considered.

Aside from population census (to which observation and photography from the air probably has the most important single application), habitat mapping, and migration, there are a number of other potential fields within animal ecology where air photography can be usefully employed. A list of such fields would include, among others;

Age distribution of populations.
Density of populations.
Distribution and dispersion.
Record of population fluctuations.
Record of population dispersal.

Plate 45. Herd of caribou (Rangifer caribou) *at Ghost Lake, MacKenzie District, Northwest Territories, Canada.* 1949

Plate 45. Herd of caribou

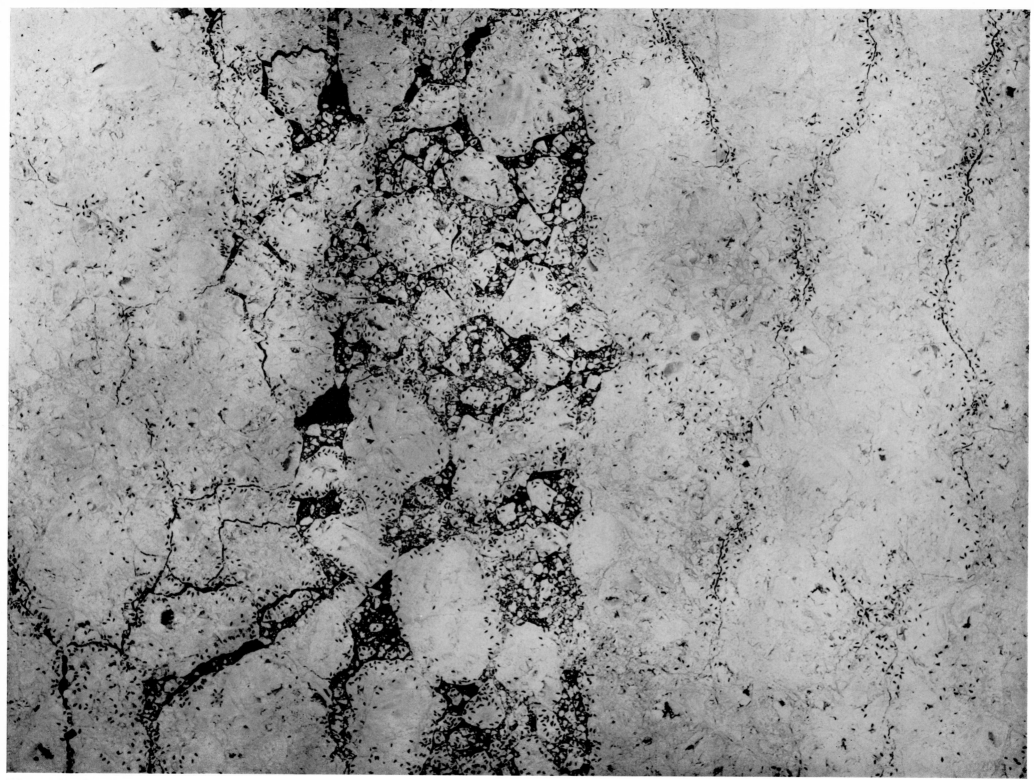

Plate 46.   Moulting harp seals on pack-ice

Population structure: territoriality, isolation, aggregation.
Food-habit surveys.

One of the most interesting examples of a survey of food-habits was graphically described in an article by D. L. Allen and L. Mech on the wolf-moose relationships on Isle Royal.[1] The authors observed from the air the winter predation of a pack of fifteen wolves on the island's moose population. They were able to watch *Canis lupus* 'in every phase of daily activity: trekking, sleeping, mating, playing, and hunting and killing moose.'

In the process of air observation Allen and Mech have been able to utilise colour photography to make a permanent record of their work. Of particular interest are the photographs illustrating the pattern of attack on moose. Although the cinematograph would have provided an even more informative record, these photographs clearly demonstrate the way in which the pack 'tests' each moose, rejecting the vigorous animal as a poor prospect in favour of a weaker individual.

This discussion of the values of air photography in biology has been limited to 'still' photography; cinematography, however, has additional value in wild-life research which should be briefly mentioned. Through slow-motion projection, the researcher is able to examine in detail locomotion in individual animals, as well as rapid movements in whole populations. Just as normal air photography has not yet been utilised as extensively as direct observation from the air, so air cinematography in biological research has been relatively little used in comparison with photographs individually taken.

So we come to our conclusion. Although the use of air photography in biological work has increased significantly in recent years, there is much room for expansion and ramification. Up till now the major use of air photographs in biology has been in vegetation mapping and for census work, particularly of big game and waterfowl. Other uses have also emerged as significant: game-range determinations, lake and stream surveys, successional studies, habitat surveys, law enforcement, refuge locations, food-habit surveys, population-age distribution, and records of population behaviour.

For the greatest returns negative as well as positive aspects of the technique must be taken into account. The needs and limitations of air photography in wild-life studies have been evaluated by Leedy as follows:

Much is to be learned regarding the type of aircraft, camera equipment, film, filters, and conditions under which aerial photographs can be taken most effectively for use in the fields of wild-life and recreation. Consideration must be given to cost of operation; season of the year and best time of day for photography to distinguish between vegetation-types or show concentrations of game species; the height at which an aircraft can be flown above animal concentrations such as waterfowl-flocks without disturbing them; and the amount of ground checking necessary to obtain the desired results.[21]

Progress has already been made in the use of these methods, but, we must reiterate, their full potential application is yet to be realised.

Plate 46. Moulting harp seals (Phoca groenlandica) *on pack-ice east of Labrador. In 1960 air photography yielded an estimate of 327,000 breeding adults in the Gulf of St Lawrence and on the 'Front', the area east of Newfoundland and southern Labrador. This figure is reported to represent a decline of over 50 per cent in ten years. Population studies based upon the evidence of air photographs are indispensible for devising a system of control of commercial sealing, essential if stocks are not to suffer virtual extinction.*
Aero Photo Inc. vertical photograph A446, print No. 47.
Scale 1 : 1,900.   *22 April 1963*

SELECTED BIBLIOGRAPHY

[1] ALLEN, D. L. and MECH, D. L., 'Wolves versus Moose on Isle Royale', *Nat. Geogr. Mag.* **123** (1963), 200-19.
[2] ANDERSON, M. and MURDY, R., 'A Comparison of Methods of Estimating Duck Brook Density', 15th Midwest Wild-life Conference (1953).
[3] BANFIELD, A. W. F., FLOOK, D. F., KELSALL, J. P. and LOUGHREY, A. G., 'Aerial Survey Technique for Northern Big Game', *N.A. Wild-life Conf.* **20** (1955), 519-32.
[4] BROWN, D. L., 'Census and Management of Central Montana Antelope', *Proc. 34th Ann. Conf. Western Assoc. State Game and Fish Commissions* (1954), 211-15.
[5] CAIN, S., 'Aerial Survey Studies of Natural Resources', *Arid Zone* **21** (1963), 8-9.
[6] CARLS, N., *How to Read Aerial Photographs for Census Work.* Dept. Commerce, Bureau of the Census (1947).
[7] CHASE, D. and SPURR, S. H., 'Photo-interpretation Aids', U.S. Forest Service, Lake States For. Exp. Sta. Report No. 38, *Wild-life Review* **81** (1955), 2.
[8] CHATTIN, J. E., 'Appraisal of California Waterfowl Concentration by Aerial Photography', *N. Amer. Wild-life Conference* **17** (1952), 421-6.
[9] CRISSEY, W. F., 'The Airplane in Fish and Game Work', *Fish and Wildl. Inf. Bull.* No. 4, New York Conservation Dept. (1949), 1-20.
[10] DARLING, F. FRASER, 'An Ecological Reconnaissance of the Mara Plains in Kenya Colony', *Wild-life Monographs* (1960), 5.

[11] EDWARDS, R. Y., 'Comparison of an Aerial and Ground Census of Moose', *J. Wildlife Management* 18 (1954), 403-4.

[12] ENG, R. L., 'Use of Aerial Coverage in Sage Grouse Strutting Ground Counts', *Proc. 34th Ann. Conf. Western Assoc. Sta. Game and Fish Commissions* (1954), 231-3.

[13] FULLER, W. A , 'Aerial Surveys for Beaver in the Mackenzie District, Northwest Territories', *N. Amer. Wild-life Conf.* 18 (1953), 329-35.

[14] GRIFFIN, D. R. and HOCK, R. J., 'Airplane Observations of Homing Birds', *Ecology* 30 (1949), 176-98.

[15] HOLWEG, A. W., 'Aerial Beaver Survey', *N.Y. Sta. Conservationist* 8 (1954), 13.

[16] HOST, PER, 'Report on Studies of the Seal Herds off Newfoundland, Spring 1950'. Unpublished report to the Conservation Foundation, 1950.

[17] KATZ, A. H., 'Aerial Photographic Equipment and Applications to Reconnaissance', *J. Optical Soc. Amer.* 38 (1948), 604-10.

[18] KELEZ, G. B., 'Measurement of Salmon Spawning by means of Aerial Photography', *Pacific Fisherman* 45 (1947), 46, 49-51.

[19] KENYON, K. W., SCHEFFER, V. B., and CHAPMAN, D. G., 'A Population Study of the Alaska Fur-Seal Herd', *U.S. Fish and Wildlife Service Special Sci. Repts.* 12 (1954).

[20] LEEDY, D. Y., 'Aerial Photographs, their Interpretation and Suggested uses in Wildlife Management', *J. Wildlife Management* 12 (1948), 191-210.

[21] LEEDY, D. L., 'Aerial Photo. Use and Interpretation in the Fields of Wildlife and Recreation', *Photogrammetric Engineering* 19 (1952), 127-37.

[22] MATTESON, C. P., 'Five-year Summary Report, Central Flyway Aerial Waterfowl Counts in Colorado', *Colorado Game and Fish Department, Current Report* 29 (1952).

[23] PETRIDES, G. A., 'Applying Principles of Naval Aircraft Recognition to Wildlife Study', *J. Wildlife Management* 8 (1944), 258-9.

[24] PETRIDES, G. A., 'Aerial Deer Counts', *J. Wildlife Management* 17 (1953), 97-8.

[25] SCHULTZ, V., 'An Application of Aerial Photography to Land-use and Cover Mapping', *J. Wildlife Management* 16 (1952), 227-8.

[26] SPINNER, G. P., 'Improved Method for Estimating Numbers of Waterfowl', *J. Wildlife Management* 10 (1946), 365.

[27] SPINNER, G. P., 'Efficiency of the Photographic Guide Method in Increasing Accuracy in Estimating Numbers of Waterfowl', *Proc. Washington D.C., Section Wildl. Soc. 9th Ann. Conf.* (1953), 1-8.

[28] WILSON, H. L. and BERARD, E. V., 'The Use of Aerial Photographs and Ecological Principles in Cover Type Mapping', *J. Wildlife Management* 16 (1952), 320-6.

[29] WILSON, H. L. and BERARD, E. V., 'Autumn Colours, an Aid to Wildlife Cover Mapping', *J. Wildlife Management* 17 (1953), 98-9.

Plate 47. Flock of some 3,550 oystercatchers (Haematopus ostralegus) *on mud-flats at Red Bank, Morecambe Bay, Lancashire (SD467680). The object of this survey, repeated at intervals through the winter, was to study variations in the size of the flocks with a view to controlling their depredations on local oyster beds. The bird-roosts were photographed at high water from an altitude of a few hundred feet, a task presenting its own problems especially if the birds were not to be disturbed.*
V-CG 10. Vertical photograph; scale 1 : 350   17 December 1963

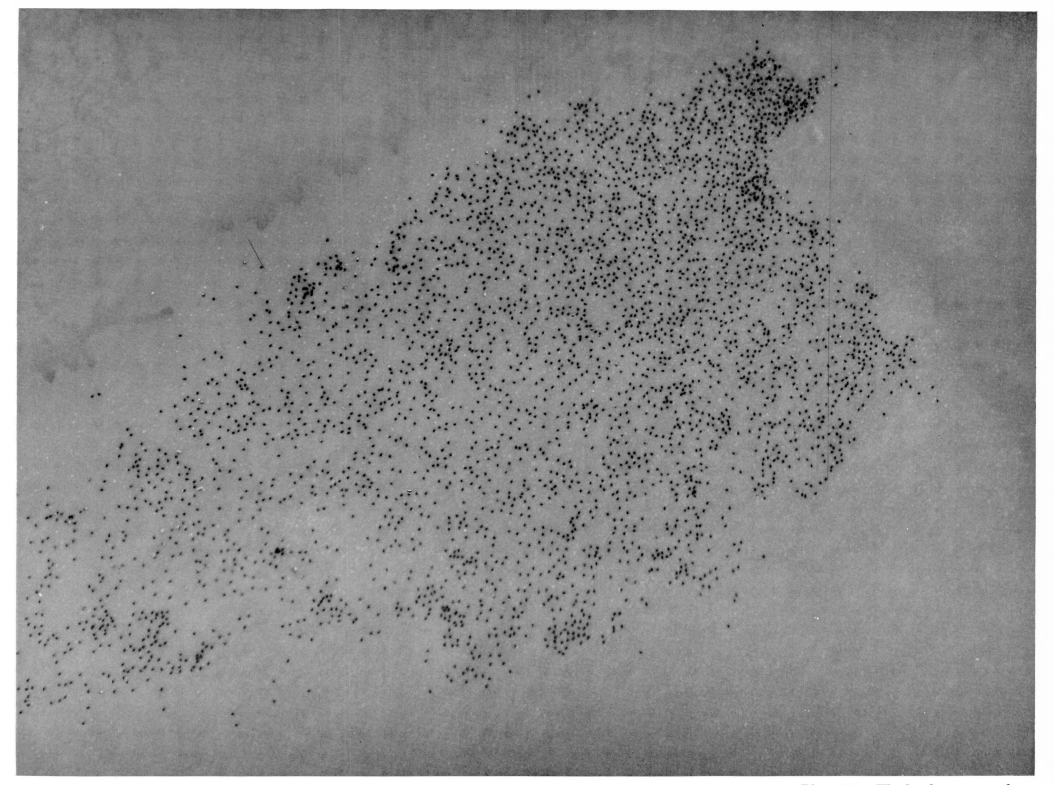

Plate 47. Flock of oystercatchers

R. M. WATSON

Air Photography in
East African Game Management and Research

IN the Serengeti National Park of northern Tanganyika a group of zoologists is studying some aspects of the ecology of this famous game area. The 'ecological unit' of the most abundant large animal of the Serengeti, the white-bearded wildebeeste, extends to some 12,000 square miles. Well over one million head of game, some relatively sedentary like the buffalo and topi-antelope, others involved in a great annual movement cycle, known as the 'migration', are found within this ecological unit. The vast size of the herds and the huge areas over which they spread has made necessary the use of a light aircraft in this research. Air photographs are indispensable for recording observations so that changing phenomena may be analysed: they also provide the only accurate means of counting hundreds of thousands of closely-packed animals.

That the boundaries of the Serengeti National Park had been drawn without regard to the migratory habits of the game has long been suspected, and is in fact confirmed by the work of the last two and a half years. In some parts of the dispersion area favoured by game in the dry season, that is to the west of the National Park, human interests are clashing directly with the interests of the Serengeti herds. Air photographs along the boundary line of the Park show haphazard scattered settlements from which the occupants are able to make regular meat-hunting excursions into the reserve. These have been used to demonstrate to the local authorities the seriousness of the problem. The very snare-lines (Plate 48) and car-tracks of intensive poaching can be seen from the air.

A common method of estimating densities of game animals in East Africa is the 'road strip transect'. This involves counting all animals within a specified distance of a road. However, a road presents a dry, bare surface on which animals may sit and dust themselves; and, rain-water collects in ruts and depressions, so that the road offers a very favourable local modification of the habitat for many species, and counts obtained in this way may not safely be treated as random samples of densities of animals throughout the whole habitat traversed by the road. Air photographs taken for census purposes often show a clustering of animals on and close to roads much denser than in their natural habitat. The difference may be as great as a factor of twenty times. The range of information derived from air observation that can be graphically presented in photographs may be judged from these examples.

The potential value of air photography in providing evidence of mistakes in land use is very great, since East Africa is a region of undeveloped countries with expanding populations, largely living in semi-arid climates. But photographs will prove of equal value in ensuring better planning in the use of land, to the benefit of National Parks and Game Reserves. The most important problem facing most game areas

Plates 48–52 are all oblique views taken with a Leica camera from altitudes below 1,000 feet.

Plate 48. North of Serengeti National Park, northern Tanzania. The irregular dark line across the centre of the photograph is a line of cut thorn-branches lying on the ground, to direct animals towards the few gaps, in which snares of steel wire are set. On the right, the track of a buffalo can be seen crossing the snare-line towards a small pool of water partly obscured by a tree-top.   *October 1963*

Plate 48.   Game trap

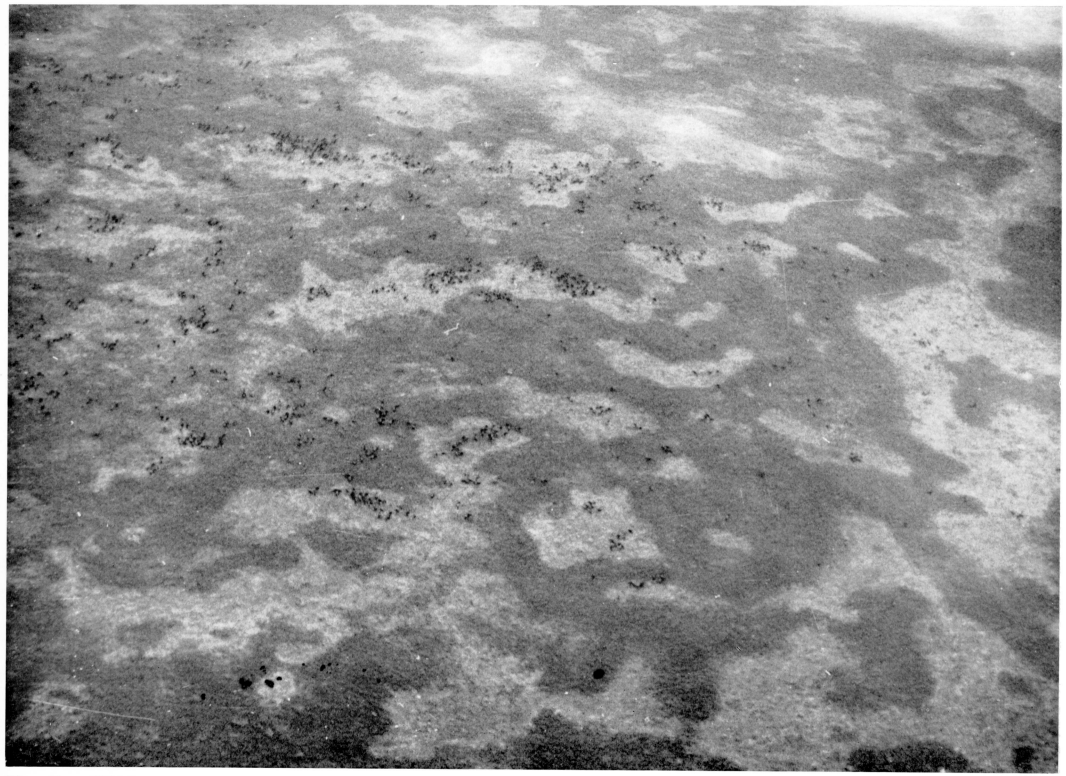

Plate 49a.   Wildebeeste (*for explanation see page 126*)

Plate 49b.   Wildebeeste and zebra

in East Africa in the next ten years will be that of land use; human populations will wish to settle and to cultivate land right up to the legal limits of Parks and Reserves; but because much of the land surrounding these protected areas is a part of the range of existing stocks of wild animals, necessary for their well-being, and because reserves within the present boundaries do not hold all the requirements of the game populations living in the reserves for most of the year, planned development of the land is much needed.

Considered as an observation platform an aircraft has the disadvantage that it cannot be held stationary; much work on ungulate groups is made very difficult by the constant movement of the animals. The air photograph provides a solution to this problem and becomes

---

Plate 49a. Serengeti National Park. Densely packed wildebeeste (Connochaetes taurinus albojubatus) are sitting and ruminating. Note the relation between the groups of animals and the light-toned patches of vegetation. These lighter patches are associations in which Andropogon greenwayii *is the dominant species. The* Andropogon *forms a close cover just above the ground surface, and never grows more than about one inch above the ground. It forms a far more comfortable surface than the darker patches of vegetation, which are associations of* Penisetum mezianum *with various herbaceous non-grasses* (Crotalaria spinosa *and* Indigofera baseflora). *Here, the vegetation is from six inches to one foot in height, and would be likely to stay damp after rain much longer than the adjacent short grasses.* May 1963

Plate 49b. Serengeti National Park. In this steep oblique photograph, taken as part of a regular analysis of population structure, three zebra families (ringed) *are seen moving at an angle to the line taken by roving wildebeeste. These families comprise:*

1	2	3
1 stallion	1 stallion	1 stallion
2 mares	4 mares	4 mares
2 foals	2 foals	2 foals
		(This family may be incomplete.)

In zebra families, the stallion characteristically takes up a position at the back of a moving group, often some little way off (families 1 and 2). *The senior mare always leads the group and is typically positioned in family 2. On the evidence of the photograph alone it would not be possible to distinguish between the mares and the stallions.* March 1964

a tool in the analysis of the activities of ungulates and of their population-structure. A typical, well defined 'activity pattern' seen in distinct groups of animals on a single photograph, is that observable when rutting is in progress. With wildebeeste, such configurations are regularly seen from mid-April to June; with topi, similar patterns occur in December and January. The composition of rutting groups in terms of adults and calves has been determined from air photographs. The number of animals in each group is easily counted. A whole range of other 'activity patterns' has been worked out, largely for the wildebeeste, and future activities can even be forecast from the configuration at any particular time. A set of reference patterns has been prepared from photographs, and these patterns are suitable for expression in mathematical terms. On all flights over wildebeeste the observer now describes the pattern of the wildebeeste according to the reference set. This standardises observations, and makes information brought back by untrained observers much more valuable. For example, Plate 49a shows a transient resting pattern of a rapidly moving group; Plates 49b, 50, 51, and 52 show various movement patterns in rapidly moving groups.

Plate 49a is a particularly interesting record of one aspect of the behaviour of wildebeeste since it demonstrates that the animals, which are sitting and ruminating, have selected one special part of the habitat (the lighter patches of vegetation). Other examples of such a preference exercised by wildebeeste are their habits of standing or sitting, which only take place on bare areas whether of natural origin, or man-made; of grazing, which is confined to areas having particular assemblages of grasses; of movement, which tends to follow already existing tracks; and of standing under trees which afford particularly dense shade in the dry season. All these phenomena, which illustrate the ability of the animal to select small sub-habitats within the larger 'habitat-type', were indeed suspected from observation on the ground and in the air, but the air photograph alone provides confirmation in a quantitative way.

In considering the structure of the whole animal population, as opposed to small parts of the population involved in particular activities such as rutting, the air photograph has become a tool for sampling as well for analysis. In March 1964 the population of wildebeeste in the

---

Plate 50. Serengeti National Park. In this photograph, which shows ideal pattern and illumination for counting, 2,003 wildebeeste are visible. The single animal below the main group, and the scattered animals in the distance, are probably all bulls, since bulls tend to move in more open formation. May 1963

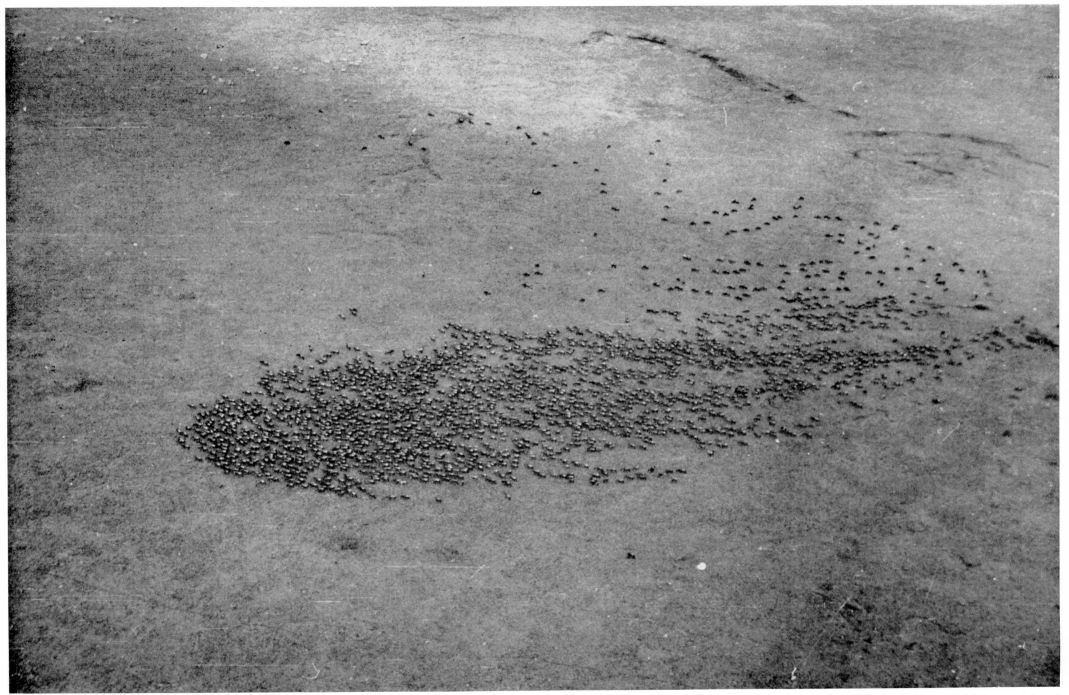

Plate 50.   Wildebeeste herd

Serengeti stood at 450,000. This is one single, migratory 'population', which throughout the year ranges over some 12,000 square miles of territory. Although observations made on the ground of the structure of the population in terms of calves, yearlings, young, mature, and old animals (the last three classes being categorised also by sex) yield much more information than can at present be obtained from air photographs, it is extremely difficult to sample satisfactorily from the ground, for various reasons. First, the fact that there is a segregation within the population of groups differing in age and sex (groups of 10,000 young bulls are typical) means counting very large numbers of animals and travelling great distances to obtain a fair sample. Secondly, the preference of different groups for different parts of the habitat leads to a wide geographical separation of these groups at some times of the year. Thus, in August 1963, most of the cows with calves were concentrated 40 miles south of the centre of concentration of cows without calves; bulls were scattered with both groups, and also concentrated, together with yearlings, up to 100 miles further south. Thirdly, cows (especially cows with calves) have a much greater flight-distance than bulls, whereas yearlings of both sexes are attracted by the approach of a car. Air photographs designed to sample variations in the structure of the population are now taken at fixed intervals along predetermined compass-courses planned to cover the major wildebeeste concentrations.

The migratory wildebeeste are particularly interesting ungulates in that no fixed herds of particular individuals are formed. The nearest approach to fixed herd structure is in rutting, but the rutting group may only exist for a few hours. This loose social structure makes the wildebeeste a promiscuous animal, even by ungulate standards. Zebra, on the other hand, have a most rigid social structure of families, consisting of one stallion and a number of foals and mares. The family varies in number from two to about fifteen individuals. In addition, groups of young males form herds of about the same size. Air photographs show this family structure very clearly (Plates 49b and 51); sometimes even the composition of the families can be seen.

The counting of herds of game animals comprising 100,000 or more individuals has to be carried out by means of air photographs. Even local counts of small populations require air photography, if the animals are at all closely packed. On the basis of almost a thousand hours flying experience in such work either as pilot or as observer, the writer's opinion is that most 'counts' of game in East Africa which involve large numbers of animals were in reality estimates, because photography was not used. In photographing total populations of wild animals one of the most important considerations is the time of year for the census. This may determine the spacing, density, shape and even the size of groups or herds. In migratory populations the possibility of movement during the counting period is an important factor. If the animal has a well defined breeding-season this will need to be considered. If the range of the animal covers open and closed terrain, the photography will need to be undertaken at a time when the animal is most visible. All the above factors are specific both for the species and the region. In counting the migratory wildebeeste of the Serengeti a period of about ten days at the end of May is thought to be the most suitable time. At this period the wildebeeste are massed in one or two areas of concentration, just before their great westward movement off the plains and into dispersion areas of bush and permanent waters favoured in the dry season. Groups vary in size from 2,000 to 50,000 with a close clustering of animals in the groups. The larger groups have a pronounced long axis, which lends itself to coverage with a single series of photographs. Immediately before the main migration the animals move but little and the terrain is completely open. Calving is finished. Photographs can be mainly taken from 800 to 1,000 feet with a camera such as a Leica, fitted with a 50 mm. lens. The smaller groups are ideal for photography because they can be recorded on a single view (Plate 50). Larger groups are photographed in an overlapping series of views taken down the long axis of the group; the amount of overlap is identified on enlarged prints from which the actual counting is made (Plate 52), so that duplication is avoided. Counting the animals calls for special care. Enlarged photographs on glossy paper are examined with a hand lens, and as each animal is counted its image is pricked by a fine needle. The small depression in the glazed surface of the print is easily visible in good light, and the print may still be used for further analysis. The illumination of the animal on the ground is an important feature to be considered when photographing animals for identification and census.

Plate 51. Serengeti National Park. One photograph taken from an overlapping series. The formation of single-file lines by the wildebeeste, seen on the left, and towards the top, shows that this is a rapidly moving group, and movement is mainly in the direction of the lines, from right to left. The local concentration of animals at the periphery of the whole group is a typical pattern, indicating that a slower grazing movement is taking the group towards the area at the bottom of the photograph. Nine or ten zebra families are scattered among the wildebeeste. 4,031 wildebeeste and 62 zebra are recorded on this print. *May 1963*

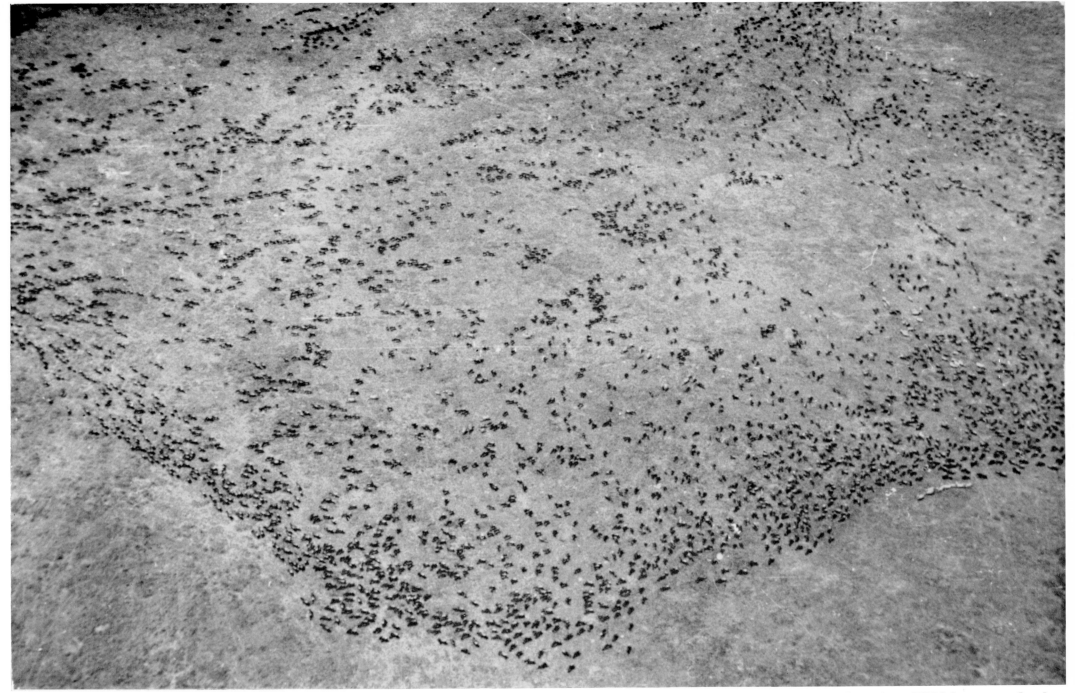

Plate 51. Wildebeeste and zebra

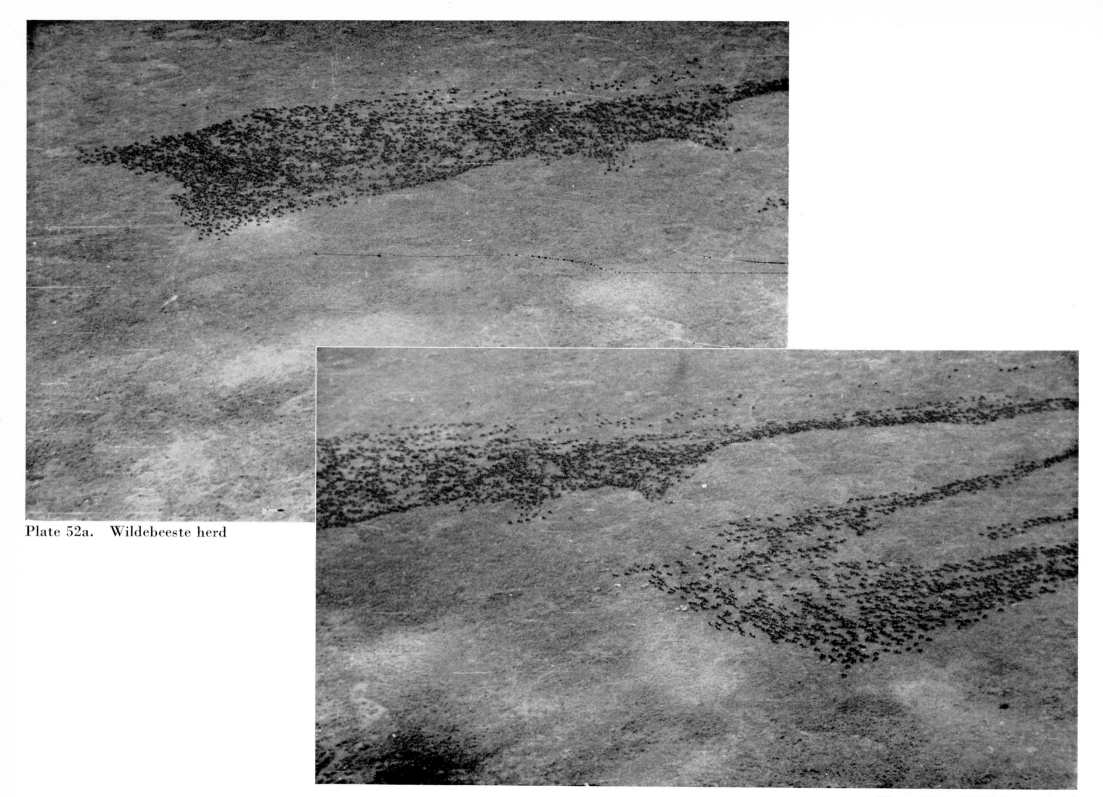

Plate 52a.   Wildebeeste herd

Plate 52b.   Wildebeeste herd

In bright, oblique sunlight wildebeeste show a distinct central reflecting highlight in the middle of the back, and the rest of the animal forms a dark surround. Zebra on the other hand appear completely white, with a dark fringing shadow. Gazelle are invisible except in certain conditions of oblique light, when they appear as rather shapeless bright spots, with little or no shadow.

This summary of the uses of air photography in one particular game study gives some idea of the potential range of application. Published accounts of such techniques in ecology tend to indicate that air photography is most valuable as a medium of illustration, but in fact there is scope for its much wider application in the analysis and sampling of animal communities. To obtain a census, photography is acknowledged as being the only possible method with large populations, for which a sampling method is not applicable.

All the work in the Serengeti has been carried out with a Cessna 150 aircraft,[1] and more recently with a Piper Super Cub. So far only oblique photography with hand-held miniature cameras has been possible: the introduction of vertical photography would be of immense value, not only for census work, but also for ecological research in its widest aspects.

NOTE

[1] M. I. M. Turner and R. M. Watson, 'Game Management and Research by Aeroplane', *Oryx* 8 (1965), 13-22, Plates i-vii.

Plate 52a and b. Serengeti National Park. Two adjacent prints in an overlapping series. The high density within the group of animals and the elongated pattern are typical of rapid movement. A good deal of line-formation is taking place; see especially the lower print. A number of zebra families can be seen. The total number of wildebeeste visible on the photographs is 5,058. *May 1963*

Plate 53.   Fornham All Saints

J. K. S. St JOSEPH

Air Photography and Archaeology

THE application of air photography to archaeology goes back at least to the 1914-18 war, when the opportunities for flying that then became available brought new awareness of the comprehensiveness of the aerial view.[1] It came to be realised that the same skill devoted to scrutinising the earth's surface for signs of enemy activity could be applied to interpreting natural and artificial features of the landscape. The value of this method for the study of ancient sites was appreciated by a number of airmen, by no means all of them archaeologists. There were, for example, Colonel Beazeley, a professional soldier who secured some of the earliest air photographs of the great buried cities of the Mesopotamian plain; Major Allen, an engineer who subsequently formed a pioneer collection of air photographs of the Oxford region; and Dr Crawford, later to become the first Archaeology Officer of the Ordnance Survey, who was the chief exponent of this method of research in the period between the wars. Soon it came to be realised that, as applied to archaeology, the aerial camera is a remarkably versatile instrument, capable not only of recording visible features with new precision and emphasis, but also of discovering buried sites of which no traces whatever are ordinarily visible to an observer on the ground.

The work of these pioneers established the principles of this method of research. Under suitable conditions an air photograph records both the existing landscape, and earlier stages of its long development either by Nature or by man. Thus it is possible to trace on air photographs many phases of man's past and present activities—social, economic and military—and also innumerable aspects of his natural background. For the greater part of the long succession of Stone Age cultures no man-made structures ordinarily survive, but air photography proves of value for the study even of these remote ages, for it can effectively display geographical factors that have determined a choice of site, thus limiting the search for ancient settlements.

Far more rewarding, however, is the application of air photography to the discovery and elucidation of man-made structures of all periods of archaeology from the Neolithic to the Middle Ages. The technique depends upon the nature of the remains. Where features occur in relief, such as mounds, banks and ditches, the most telling photographs are obtained by paying attention to the effects of sunlight and shadows (Plates 60, 64). Oblique sunlight can emphasise small differences in relief: with a complicated site several photographs from different directions and at different times of day may be necessary. The number and variety of earthworks, particularly those of the Middle Ages, surviving in Britain can only be appreciated by flying at a relatively low altitude under conditions of crisp clear sunlight in early morning or late evening, when minor variations in the surface are picked out in a detail which never fails to astonish, so that the form of the ground takes on new meaning.

Modern agriculture involves both deep ploughing of established arable land and the breaking up of so-called 'marginal land', now being first brought under cultivation, and so inevitably causes many ancient sites to be progressively levelled or even obliterated. In such instances no features remain to guide the field-observer and history becomes buried in level ploughed fields. Even so, ancient sites may be visible from the air as patterns in bare soil or in vegetation. Thus, variations in colour in freshly ploughed land can be a valuable source of information, particularly when a marked colour-contrast is in question. In the chalk

---

Plate 53.   Fornham All Saints, Suffolk (foreground at TL831684). A cursus, about a mile in length, and an 'interrupted ditch-system' seen in terms of crop marks. No traces whatever are visible to an observer on the ground.

ABM 9   *22 June 1960*

Plate 54.   Glenlochar, Kirkcudbrightshire

Plates 54 and 55. *Air photography as a means of discovery: the same area at Glenlochar, Kirk-cudbrightshire (NX235645), photographed in two different years. In the second plate a 5-acre Roman fort is revealed by differential growth of vegetation in a drought. Not only is the general site clearly visible but even the precise lines of the ditches, the rampart and the very streets, outlining plots for timber buildings, so that a detailed plan can be made, permitting an estimate of the size of the garrison.*
MR 67   25 July 1953
DV 65   12 July 1949

Plate 55.   Glenlochar, Kirkcudbrightshire

country of southern England remains of so called 'Celtic fields', the small arable plots being tilled at the time of Caesar's invasion, are commonly seen by reason of the difference in colour between the spread of white chalk from the field-banks, and the normal coloured soil elsewhere. Equally striking effects are provided by the contrast between the white chalk of a barrow-mound and the dark earth filling its surrounding ditch, or between the light-toned silts in the Fenland and the black peaty soil of ditches cut in the silt. The scatter of building-stone, mortar and daub on the site of a medieval building, of clay or turf from the rampart of a Roman fort, or of gravel from the metalling of a Roman road, all leave characteristic marks visible from the air: the range of the effects is as wide as the variety of soils themselves.

The most important source of new information is, however, provided by differences in the growth of vegetation brought about by hidden differences in the soil beneath. Thus, the increased depth of soil filling pits, hollows, post-holes and trenches may produce a denser and taller growth of crop than the average. Foundations, floors, and road-metalling, relatively impenetrable to roots, cause poor or stunted growth. The effect is complicated: much depends upon the weather during the whole growing season, upon the soil, and upon the type of vegetation (Plates 55-9). The most striking results are obtained in a dry season, where there are marked contrasts in the soil, and when the vegetation is a long-rooted cereal like wheat, oats or barley. The observed differences vary according to the interplay of these several factors. In general, cereal crops are the most sensitive, root crops much less so, while hay and meadow-grass are unlikely to yield results in an average year. The effects are enhanced by dry weather, while exceptional drought accompanied by high temperatures so transforms the scene as to yield information on a scale hardly matched by the results of a dozen normal years. It will be appreciated that the stage of growth most sensitive to these effects comes in the second half of the growing season, that is, in Britain, usually between the end of May and early July. The development of the growth differences, or 'crop-marks' as they are called, may be watched until the clearest definition is attained: the growth over buried ditches and hollows is then usually taller and darker than normal. As the crop ripens the effect may persist as patches of green, contrasting with the yellow of the ripening corn, or the colours may become bleached. In extreme drought vegetation normally unresponsive may yield results, so that accurate plans of buried foundations may then be seen, even in grass. Nor should it be thought that the crops already mentioned are the only ones worth study. Under favourable conditions growth differences occur in many other types of vegetation and at other seasons of the year.

It should be emphasised that repeated reconnaissance is essential if the best results are to be obtained (cf. Plates 54, 55). Often a given archaeological site is covered by several fields, under a variety of crops, as the agricultural rotation brings different crops to each field in turn. Thus, buried sites may remain invisible for many years, until a combination of favourable weather in the growing season, sensitive crops suited to the particular soil, and the presence at the right time of an aircraft with trained observer and camera, yield results as unexpected as they may be varied. This chapter is written with special reference to Britain, but equally important discoveries are undoubtedly to be looked for elsewhere, once the opportunities for this work and the limitations imposed by different vegetation and varying terrain have been appreciated. Notable results have already been obtained in France, Germany and Mediterranean lands.[2]

The earliest man-made structures now surviving in Britain comprise the corrals or 'causewayed camps', as they have been called, the 'cursus' or processional avenues, and the 'henges' or religious monuments of the Neolithic communities (c. 3,000-2,000 B.C.). A small number of these 'causewayed camps' are known from the chalk hills of the south. They consist of one or more concentric rings of interrupted ditches enclosing an area which at Windmill Hill (Wiltshire), the best known site, extends to 20 acres within the outermost circuit. Comparable systems of interrupted ditches have recently been identified outside the chalk country, mostly on river gravel (Plate 53). One, at Abingdon, in Berkshire, was identified by excavation in 1933.[3] In the last few years air photography has yielded some fourteen more.

The gain in information is evident: a single site in a river valley might always be explained as an exception. Fifteen sites enable an archaeologist to consider their distribution-pattern, to see where more might be sought. Even for these early periods the air photograph may suggest a date for the remains either by relating structures to other

Plate 56. Arbury Banks, Hertfordshire (TL260387). A prehistoric settlement of the Iron Age revealed in all its astonishing complexity. Clusters of post-holes mark the position of native huts rebuilt time and again. The numerous pits, for storage, refuse or drainage, cannot all be contemporary: fresh pits will have been dug as others became soured, fouled or filled up. The crop is wheat, growing on chalk.
OM 52   *24 June 1954*

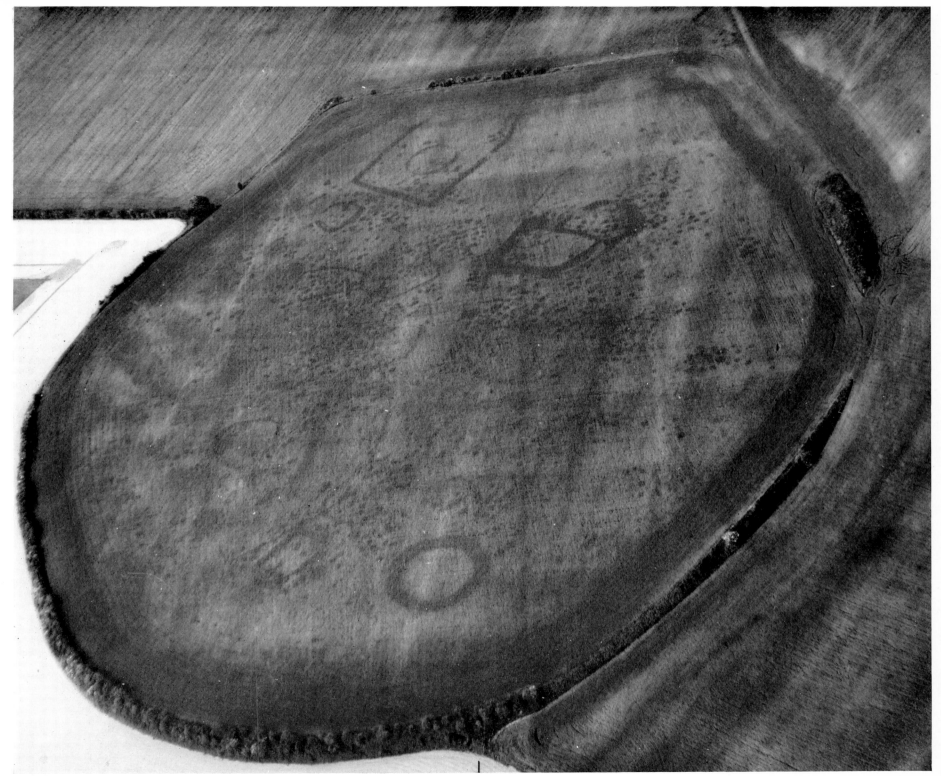

Plate 56. Arbury Banks

monuments of known character or by demonstrating significant associations. Knowledge of the *cursus*, of which two, near Stonehenge and on Gussage Down, Dorset, alone remain as substantial earthworks, has been transformed by air photography. Before the last war six further examples had come to light, mainly due to pioneer reconnaissance by Major Allen of the middle Thames valley. Since then at least thirteen more *cursus* have been recognised, extending the known distribution of these monuments to Yorkshire and even to Scotland. The religious monuments known as 'henges' are in the form of great earthen enclosures consisting of a ditch and bank that define a circle or oval with one or two entrances. Uprights in timber or stone, as at the more sophisticated examples, were not always present. Reconnaissance during the last fifteen years has yielded fully a dozen 'henges' unknown before.

These few instances of the application of air photography to the study of the oldest man-made structures surviving in Britain suffice to show something of the opportunities and limitations of this method of research. Knowledge of the distribution of given classes of monument and, by implication, of the people who made them is greatly widened. Occasionally the air photograph throws different structures into direct visual relationship (as at Thornborough, in Yorkshire, where the Middle Ring is seen to overlie a *cursus*),[4] thus establishing their relative ages, or showing where the question can be settled by digging. Again, the number of such monuments available for scientific excavation and study either by field-work or by excavation is greatly increased. At some sites features are, indeed, visible above ground yet were first identified from the air. It may come as a surprise to the reader that there exist monuments several hundred feet across, comprising a bank 20 to 30 feet wide still standing a few feet high, that have remained unrecorded till now. The 'henges' at Nunwick and at Burton Fleming in Yorkshire, are examples of the rewards that await the field observer: there are many areas of Britain that remain archaeologically unexplored.

The round barrows (burial-mounds) of the Bronze Age are amongst the commonest of ancient earthworks on the chalk of Salisbury Plain and the Yorkshire Wolds. The hard, compact chalk weathers slowly, and failing human interference a substantial mound may remain almost indefinitely. Over the years, however, the deep tractor-ploughing of modern agriculture, not to mention deliberate levelling, have taken their toll, the smallest earthworks vanishing most quickly. Away from the chalk, the regions most densely settled by early man were the river-valleys and sandy heaths, where light soils supported vegetation less dense than that of the clay lands. The gravel and sands of these areas are much more liable to weathering than compacted chalk, and earthworks built of such lighter materials are more easily denuded and levelled by long-continued ploughing: until the advent of air photography there was no means of estimating the loss to archaeology from the destruction of ancient sites.

Continued ploughing may destroy a mound and cause a ditch to be filled in, but does not interfere with features below the depth reached by the ploughshare. Thus, every structure cut deep enough into the sub-soil, like the circular ditch round a barrow, may be seen from the air as a mark in soil or crops, even though surface features have been smoothed away. It has long been clear that the surviving barrows are but a fraction of the number that formerly existed. The results of a comparatively few hours' air reconnaissance of a region comprising part of north-east Essex and east Suffolk, including the valleys of the Colne, Stour, Gipping and Deben, may be taken as a specific example. The distribution of barrows marked on the large-scale Ordnance survey maps is shown on Fig. 4. No doubt, search in the records of local museums might add a few more but not enough greatly to change the pattern. Two of these barrows are the well-known Belgic burial-mounds on Lexden Heath: the group of ten barrows south-east of Woodbridge which include the famous Sutton Hoo ship-burial are of Dark Age date, as are one or two others. When these have been deducted from the total there remain some forty-eight examples, apparently dating to the Bronze Age as far as can be seen from surface inspection. Fig. 5 shows, in addition, all the ring-ditches (representing ploughed-out barrows) identified in reconniassance flights, spread over several years but amounting to not more than a few hours in total duration. The majority were recorded in the exceptionally dry summer of 1959. The number of sites has risen from 48 to 250, an increase of over 400 per cent. It is interesting to speculate what might have been inferred from Fig. 4 about the actual distribution of such barrows. Probably all would have agreed that the pattern was very incomplete, but there is no hint of penetration inland, no suspicion of dense occupation of the river-valleys, no suggestion of any connexion with the Breckland, the other area in East Anglia where barrows are relatively densely grouped. Such is the gain in knowledge yielded by carefully planned surveys in one region, and in one minor aspect of archaeology.

Undoubtedly the distribution pattern is still far from complete: continuance of this work will certainly yield more discoveries, but it is well to emphasise that already much of the country is lost forever to archaeological reconnaissance from the air. The built-up areas of towns

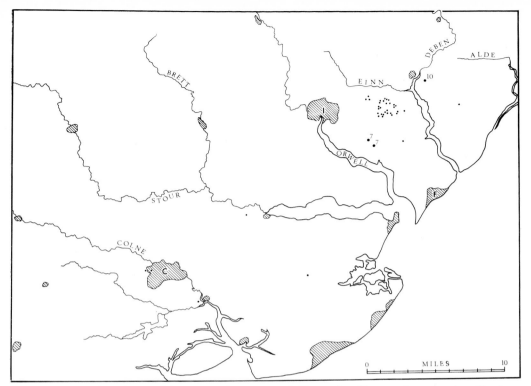

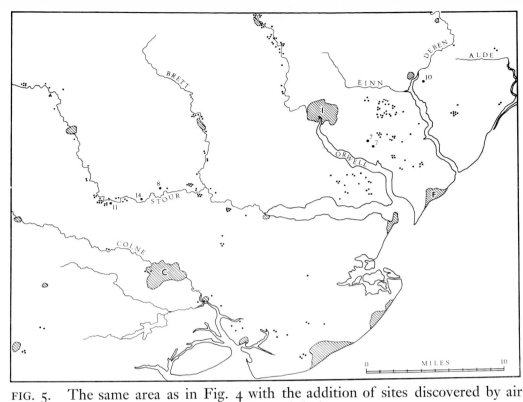

FIG. 4.   Distribution of barrows in part of East Anglia, as known in Spring, 1959.

FIG. 5.   The same area as in Fig. 4 with the addition of sites discovered by air reconnaissance, mainly in 1959.

Each small dot represents one barrow; a large dot with a figure beside it marks a group of that number of barrows. Built-up areas of towns are marked by shading.
C = Colchester, F = Felixstowe, I = Ipswich.

and villages, the woodlands, orchards and market-gardens, the innumerable scattered farms and country-houses, must account for a large proportion, perhaps over a quarter, of the total area.

Before the advent of air photography the known monuments of the Iron Age consisted largely of the great earthworks comprising the tribal *oppida*, or hill-forts, that crown so many of the chalk hills in southern England, and of the slighter earthworks of the contemporary settlements with their corn-plots, or 'Celtic fields' as they have come to be called. But whereas the hill-forts are mostly so large that visible features survive even if denuded and sometimes damaged, the settlements and their fields are easily levelled by modern agriculture and are now only to be seen in those few areas scarcely touched by modern ploughing. In the 'Highland Zone' of Wales and the North, factors that determine the modern use of land operate so as to favour the preservation of hill-forts and settlements in moorland terrain, while in the fertile valleys earthworks tend to be destroyed.

Air photography makes a three-fold contribution to the study of major earthworks like the hill-forts:[5] firstly, the recognition that at many sites the defences are the result of a long and complicated structural development; secondly, the revelation that there exist hill-forts that remain unfinished and display even today the methods of their builders; and thirdly, the recording under favourable conditions of the very hut-positions, pits and drainage-channels within these hill-forts, so furnishing information from which to assess the detailed economy of these great *oppida*.

The progress of this work in the last few years demonstrates that the hill-forts and settlements of the chalk downland and of the 'Highland Zone' represent only one element in the picture of Iron Age Britain. Air photography is transforming our knowledge of the distribution of Iron Age settlements, bringing to earthworks already known a new understanding and yielding new sites on a scale almost beyond belief and expectation. It is evident that many settlements existed both in the chalk country and in the main river-valleys where no earthworks remain visible to the field observer.

119

Plate 57. Thorpe Achurch

Plate 57. Thorpe Achurch, Northampton-shire (TL026824). The plan of this Belgic settlement is seen almost with the clarity of an engineer's blue-print.
ZA 95   26 June 1959

Plate 58. Strageath, Perthshire (NN898180). The ditch-systems of a series of superimposed Roman forts are visible. The value of such a photograph to an excavator planning the inves-tigation of so complicated a site is evident. The crop giving this amazingly clear rendering of buried features is oats. The ditches continue be-neath the rest of the field (bottom half of the plate), but the root-crop growing there is insensitive to buried remains.
V-BC 57. Vertical photograph; scale 1 : 1,700
                                          26 July 1962

Plate 58.   Strageath

The valley gravels of the larger rivers in central England are seen to have been densely populated, and only now is it becoming possible to assess the range and extent of this information.[6] Marks in the growing crops are the sole clue to the existence of these settlements, which appear sometimes scattered, sometimes in small groups. Not only the boundary-ditches of settlements but under favourable conditions even the post-holes of native huts, of granaries and other structures, besides storage-pits and field-enclosures, appear in unexpected detail. Two illustrations must suffice to demonstrate the character and extent of this information. The ring-earthwork known as Arbury Banks, in Hertfordshire, enclosing some twelve acres, has long been known, and in an average year little more is visible from the air than on the ground. However, Plate 56, taken in drought, shows, in the interior, compounds defined by ditches, and superimposed circles of post-holes where one native hut has succeeded another on the same site. Regular settings of post-holes suggest corn-drying racks or granaries, while the maze of pits, probably mostly for storage, points to prolonged occupation, fresh pits being dug to replace earlier ones as they became soured, fouled or filled up. The air photograph thus presents the site not at any given stage of develop-ment but in the totality of its remains, and the value to an excavator is evident in telling him what he is going to find and where to find it. Plate 57 illustrates by contrast a settlement of more sophisticated charac-ter at Thorpe Achurch in the Nene Valley where there is greater elabor-ation of planning. This may prove to be a Belgic farmstead belonging to the closing phases of the Iron Age, when a people employing new techniques and better material equipment were bringing fresh soils under cultivation. Here the minor detail is less in evidence, but all these sites have to be viewed with the eye of historical imagination which interprets visible features in the light of all available evidence, particularly that of excavated examples. Many small-scale structures promote such minor differences in the soil as to be visible on air photographs only in optimum conditions, while details like dry thorn-hedges (used as boundaries for stock-enclosures) may leave no trace. Such rural com-munities persisted in the remoter parts of the country long into the Roman age, the period when the evidence of the written word first became significant, marking for Britain the start of history.

What, it may be asked, is the contribution of air photography to our knowledge of Roman Britain, already studied by generations of archaeo-logists and for which written sources are available to supplement archaeological evidence? The answer may be briefly summarised.[7] Between the Thames and the Trent air reconnaissance has yielded many new military sites of first importance for studying the initial phases of the Roman conquest, for which literary sources are meagre. In the principal military zones of Wales and the North air photography has literally changed the map, revealing forts and camps in numbers beyond all expectation. In four sorties over Scotland in August 1945, involving comparatively few hours' flying, more military sites were discovered than had come to light by observation on the ground since the work of General Roy two centuries before. Such a rate of discovery cannot be maintained, but reconnaissance of the same region in each successive year continues to reveal sites hitherto unknown, as well as new information about places already known, so that more military sites in Roman Scotland have now been found by air photo-graphy than by any other means. The implications, both for the military history of the province, and for the study of individual campaigns, are far-reaching. A picture emerges of the boldness of Roman strategy supplemented by a wealth of evidence (Plates 55, 58) about the technical skill of military engineers at the peak of the Roman army's power and prestige, revealed by a variety of military sites of the late first and second century not easily matched in any other frontier-province of the Empire.

In the civil zone of Roman Britain there is abundant new inform-ation about both towns and countryside. Thus, at a number of the tribal capitals, Wroxeter, St Albans, Silchester and Caistor-by-Norwich, air photography has yielded a virtually complete plan of streets and build-ings in stone for large sections of the built-up area. At Silchester and Caistor important new information concerning the development of the town defences has come to light. At the smaller towns there has been a corresponding gain in information. In the countryside the discovery of many *villae* provides important new opportunities for the study of these establishments by excavation using modern techniques. The sites of numerous rural communities marked by buildings in timber or stone, by

Plate 59. Dorchester, Oxfordshire (SU589945). This site lies on gravel above the flood-plain of the river Thame, two-thirds of a mile east of Dorchester Abbey. Within the right-hand enclosure are a large number of small regularly oriented marks, apparently graves of an early Christian cemetery. Traces of buildings, in timber, also appear, and the discovery raises the question whether this may be the site either of the College of secular canons founded in the seventh century, or of cathedral buildings established when Dorchester first became a see.
AFU 43   *25 June 1962*

Plate 59.　Dorchester

Plate 60. Kirkstead Abbey

storage-pits, and by ditches defining agricultural plots or enclosures for stock, provide a new source of information about the less Romanised part of the population. The 'Celtic fields' of Romano-British agriculture have been so damaged by ploughing in later ages that their former extent can now only be found by air photography. Recognition of the degree of Roman colonisation of the fertile soils round the Fenland margins and especially in the silt fens near Spalding has come from application of the same techniques. Here there is evidence of Roman planned land-use on a large scale, even more remarkable in its way than the familiar 'centuriation' of Mediterranean lands, for it implies that problems of land-drainage in the exceptionally flat silt Fenlands must have been mastered.

In the Dark Ages three sites call for particular mention. The two seventh-century royal vills at Yeavering and Milfield, near Wooler, in Northumberland, may be reckoned amongst the most remarkable individual discoveries that have ever come from air photography. The detailed structural features and relationship of the timber buildings at Yeavering (Plate 61) did not appear from inspection of the air photographs, and full knowledge of the complexity of the site only came from Dr Hope Taylor's excavations. Near Dorchester-on-Thames, in Oxfordshire, a cemetery with regularly orientated graves has appeared (Plate 59): buildings, probably of timber, visible nearby may mark the site either of the College of Secular Canons known to have been founded in the seventh century, or of cathedral buildings established when Dorchester first became a see.

Traces of man's activities in the Middle Ages constitute the commonest archaeological features visible on the surface of almost every English county, and may be studied with advantage and precision by means of air photography (Plates 60, 63, 64).[8] They include the sites of villages that flourished in the eleventh and twelfth centuries and are now deserted, the 'open fields' in ridge and furrow, the moats, fishponds

and boundary-earthworks of medieval estates, and the broken ground where search for such raw materials as lime, clay, marl and building-stone has scarred the surface of the land. These remains are a potential source of information for the historian complementary to that obtained from written records. Indeed, the variety of applications of this method of research to remains of the Middle Ages, as to those of later centuries, has yet to be fully realised.

NOTES

[1] For a brief account of the early history of air photography as applied to archaeology see O. G. S. Crawford and A. Keiller, *Wessex from the Air* (1928), 3-7; and J. K. S. St Joseph, 'A Survey of Pioneering in Air Photography', in *Aspects of Archaeology*, ed. W. F. Grimes (1957), 305-15. The journal *Antiquity* includes *passim* many air photographs of archaeological features, while a number of Major Allen's photographs have been published in *Oxoniensia* (vol. 1, 1936, onwards).

[2] The pioneer works of A. Poidebard, *La Trace de Rome dans le désert de Syrie* (1934), 2 vols., and (with R. Mouterde), *Le Limes de Chalcis*, 1945, 2 vols., should be consulted, as also J. Barradez, *Fossatum Africae* (1949), containing an important account of Roman frontier fortifications in Algeria. Work in progress in northern France is particularly in the hands of R. Agache, who has started a series of surveys designed to record archaeological sites in the Somme basin, *Bull. Soc. Prehist. Nord* 5 (1962); 6 (1964). In Germany, archaeological air reconnaissance of the middle Rhine valley and adjacent areas has since 1960 been organised by Dr I. Scollar at Bonn: *Archäologie aus der Luft* (Dusseldorf, 1965). The quality of the results to be obtained in Italy may be judged from J. S. P. Bradford, *Ancient Landscapes* (1957), 85-144, Plates 25-37, and from the same author's two papers in *Antiquity*, 20 (1946), 191; 23 (1949), 58. More recently, further studies have been undertaken in Italy, both by the Lerici Foundation, at Milan, and by the Istituto Geografico Militare, at Florence (Colonel G. Schmiedt).

[3] E. T. Leeds, *Antiq. J.* 14 (1934), 414-16.

[4] Second Annual Report of the Cambridge Committee for Aerial Photography, *Cambridge Univ. Reporter* 83 (1952-3), 874; N. Thomas, *Yorks. Arch. J.* 38 (1955), 427-32.

[5] For good examples of vertical photographs of hill-forts in Wessex, see Crawford and Keiller, *Wessex from the Air* (1928), Plates i-xi, pp. 36-99.

[6] This information about 'native settlements' is based upon photographs obtained since 1945 and now in the Cambridge University Collection. In the last two years, intensive air reconnaissance by Mr J. Pickering of such valleys as the Warwickshire Avon and the Trent has emphasised the density of prehistoric settlement there.

[7] For summaries of the results achieved by the application of air reconnaissance to Romano-British studies in the last twenty years, see J. K. S. St Joseph, *Journ. of Rom. Stud.* 41 (1951), 52; 43 (1953), 81; 45 (1955), 82; 48 (1958), 86; 51 (1961), 119; 55 (1965), 74.

[8] See M. W. Beresford and J. K. S. St Joseph, *Medieval England : an aerial survey* (1958).

Plate 60. Kirkstead, Lincolnshire (TF188617). These earthworks, all that now remain of this great Cistercian abbey, are seen as a confused jumble by an observer on the ground. In the distant view provided by an air photograph, taken in oblique lighting, the system becomes clear. The position of the church and of the conventual buildings grouped round two or more cloisters may be distinguished, together with out-buildings, moats and fishponds.

PH 27

29 March 1955

Plate 61.   Yeavering

M. D. KNOWLES

Air Photography and History

IT may be thought that air photography as an aid to knowledge loses much of its value when history takes over from pre-history, for by definition this transition occurs when written material, as distinguished from all other physical records of the past, becomes available in adequate measure. It is true that in a fully historical epoch air photography becomes an ancillary rather than a primary source of information, but there are many topics in any period of history, even in our own contemporary life, where printed evidence is either hard to come by or is piled in masses of unmanageable size, and where an air photograph can show at a glance a particular process, such as the growth of an industrial town, isolated from all else.

In any case, we do not leap from pre-history to history in a year, or even in a century, and for much of English history before the Norman Conquest we depend upon sources other than written records. Sometimes, indeed, an air photograph can define and illuminate what is vague or insignificant in the written record. A striking example is the discovery of the historical relevance of the buildings revealed by crop marks at Milfield and at Yeavering (Plate 61) in Northumberland. These were first noticed and photographed by Dr J. K. St Joseph in 1949, and two photographs of the sites were published in 1953. They were subsequently identified with two royal vills mentioned by Bede the

Venerable in his *Ecclesiastical History* (II. xiv) and excavations at Yeavering have revealed the foundations of large timber halls and of staging apparently for a tiered auditorium.[1]

In one department of history, that of the agricultural economy, air photography is particularly valuable. The standard or classical layout of a nucleated medieval village is familiar, with its arable divided into small individual strips cultivated with the 'two-field' or 'three-field' rotation of crops, with its leys or rich grazing land for cattle, and with its waste land valuable for timber or pannage. Once attention had been drawn to the systems of medieval agriculture surviving to the present day, relics were discovered and duly described and mapped. The most familiar instance is Laxton (Nottinghamshire),[2] to which attention has been directed by a book, *The Open Fields*, by C. S. and C. S. Orwin, and subsequent filming and broadcasting. Within the past twenty years a number of early (sixteenth-century) field-maps have been published of other villages from all over the midlands and north-east England, showing the common fields and strips. Air photography has illustrated these maps in a striking way by revealing the marks of the plough at different angles corresponding to the arrangement of the strips within the area of large modern fields that have been for centuries turned over to grass. Even when the observer on foot is aware of the ridges he cannot obtain an overall sight of the terrain, nor see at a glance the correspondence between the cartographer's sketch and the lines of the furrows.

In this context an important achievement of air photography has been that of raising and solving the problem of the origins of the 'ridge-and-furrow' surface familiar to all midland countrymen. A normal answer given to local enquiry was that this arrangement was made at some unspecified date for purposes of drainage—an answer which assumed that farmers at some remote date would have engaged upon drainage works on such a scale and so universally. Air photography

Plate 62. Padbury West Field in 1591.

Plate 62. Padbury West Field in 1591, after Thomas Clerke. Comparison of the air photograph (Plate 63) with this map of the same area shows that it is possible to match each individual ridge with a corresponding strip on the Elizabethan map, which represents the 'open-field' system in being as a going concern. The map thus demonstrates that the pattern of ridge-and-furrow visible today is that of the pre-enclosure strips, and gives in addition the names of the Elizabethan tenants.

Plate 63. Padbury, Buckinghamshire (SP717302). Medieval ridge and furrow comprising a number of 'furlongs' in the West Field of Padbury. The ridges are picked out by the evening sunlight. The straight hedge-rows radiating from the village represent the work of the enclosure surveyors of 1796. Thus the photograph shows the modern field-system superimposed upon the medieval landscape of 'open fields'.

LS 58

2 May 1953

Plate 63. Padbury West Field in 1953

shows not only that ridge-and-furrow land exists where the ploughed fields of the village once lay, but also that irregular and disjointed examples of ridge-and-furrow, which could not conceivably be drainage works, exactly represent the irregular and staggered arrangement of the strips in early maps, while in many cases the original pattern of ridge-and-furrow can be seen to have been broken by subsequent (and in some cases even by medieval) buildings. No doubt examples of surfaces akin to ridge-and-furrow exist as a result of post-medieval ploughing or even of calculated drainage operations, but it is certain that in innumerable instances the ridge-and-furrow pattern is the unintentional outcome of medieval husbandry. Plates 62 and 63 show the open fields of Padbury (Buckinghamshire), with part of the map of 1591 now in the possession of All Souls College, the owners of the land. It will be noted how the ridge-and-furrow of the open fields has been intersected by the hedges planted c. 1796. In the left of photograph and, beyond the medieval field-lane, towards the right-hand margin, furrows running at right angles to the main run of the strips are visible, precluding any explanation as drainage works. Comparison with the map provides incontrovertible proof of the medieval origin of the ridge and furrow. Similar patchwork patterns of strips can be seen still more clearly in photographs (with plans) of Ilmington and Crimscote, both in Warwickshire.[3]

One of the most spectacular discoveries in medieval economic history in the past thirty years has been that of the almost ubiquitous 'deserted' village. The sites of a few such abandoned groups of habitation had of course long been known locally. Ancient tradition, the existence of a medieval parish church deep in the fields and far from human habitation, and in some cases even records of a village no longer in being had served to inform the local historian or antiquary, but in almost every case the date and cause of the abandonment were unknown, and the Black Death in one of its manifestations had been called in as an explanation. No attempt had been made to catalogue or compare the various examples. The great plagues of the fourteenth century were certainly responsible for some of the extinctions (an example is Tusmore in Oxfordshire)[4] but a more universal dissolvent was the change-over from arable to pasture between 1450 and 1550. Plate 64 shows extensive earthworks first recognised as a result of air reconnaissance. They mark the site of a deserted village at Newbold Grounds, near Catesby, in Northamptonshire. This site has never been ploughed in modern times so that the earthworks are exceptionally well preserved. The lines of streets, the crofts and buildings and the bank and ditch marking the perimeter of the village may all be distinguished, as well as the

contemporary fields in ridge-and-furrow. In the eighteenth century many open fields were enclosed 'by agreement', more or less voluntarily, or by a private Act of Parliament. The photograph of Padbury (Plate 63) shows the hedges that were then drawn over the landscape. A few villages disappeared in the process.

In medieval England religious houses must often have formed the most prominent work of human hands in a landscape. Even now the cathedrals (once abbeys) of Peterborough and Gloucester stand out above their commercial and industrial surroundings, and they must have dominated the low medieval roofs as Ely cathedral still dominates its small city. Many of the six hundred abbeys and priories stood in small hamlets or in the open country, and as the church invariably stood on the highest point of the site they must often have been visible for miles. Only a small number are intact to any degree; the remains of the others have fallen into ruins in every degree of dissolution from the imposing fragments of a Rievaulx or a Fountains to the superficial disappearance of a Sempringham or a Croxton. Air photography is not necessary to display the beauty of these ruins, situated as they often are in surroundings of exquisite natural charm, but it is valuable in at least two ways. A vertical or almost vertical photograph can present the layout and the successive alterations made to the buildings in a way that neither a plan nor a view from the ground can hope to do. Thus a view of Kirkstall (Yorkshire, W.R., actually within the built-up area of Leeds) shows the typical, regular Cistercian plan to perfection; a view of Furness (Lancashire) makes the enlargement of the cloister and the repeated alteration of the refectory comprehensible at a glance[5]; while photographs of such sites as Easby (Yorkshire, N.R.)[6] and Haughmond (Shropshire)[7] show clearly the irregularities of design that might easily be missed on the ground.

Another use of air photography in this field is an application of a technique more commonly applied to sites of prehistoric or Roman times. A view taken under optimum conditions of lighting, of drought or of crop-growth may show the existence and plan of foundations

---

Plate 64. Deserted medieval village, Newbold Grounds, Catesby, Northamptonshire (SP517606). The characteristic earthworks of a deserted village include sunken 'hollow ways' marking the lines of streets, banks and ditches defining the boundaries of crofts, and irregular low mounds covering the remains of buildings, of which the most substantial were the church and manor house.

AHG 33   *10 June 1963*

Plate 64. Deserted medieval village

not previously discovered or excavated. Several Cistercian abbeys of which little remains above ground can be reconstructed in this way. Thus Revesby and Kirkstead (Plate 60), both in Lincolnshire,[8] and Sawtry (Huntingdonshire) could be excavated in the light of air photographs already available, while parch-marks in photographs of Roberts-bridge (Sussex)[9] show the east end of the church and part of the infirmary invisible to one standing on the site. Pre-eminent in this respect is the site of the great double monastery of Sempringham (Lincolnshire), head house of the Gilbertine order. This wide complex of buildings, comprising two complete monasteries with cloisters, dorters, refectories and the rest, lying on either side of a large church in which both canons and nuns had separate choirs, must have dominated the flat landscape of the wide valley wherein it stood, and its tower or spire must have been visible from afar. All this had disappeared to the last stone, and all traditions of the site had vanished. It was even supposed that the buildings had lain some distance away near the small medieval parish church. As the site was under rough pasture before 1940 air photography was unrevealing, but the foundation trenches of the church were discovered in part by a process of cross-cutting in 1939. Then in 1950, when the land was under cereal crop, an air photograph revealed the outline not only of the church but of the claustral buildings to north and south, visible as lighter growth in the young herbage.[10]

Second only to monasteries as characteristic monuments of the medieval scene are the castles. Here air photography begins once more with its function of indication and revelation, and proceeds to that of general illustration. In historical times the castle, considered as a piece of military architecture as opposed to the camp or defensive earthwork, began as a wooden tower on an eminence, natural or artificial, surrounded by an irregular fence or ditch. This was the so-called motte-and-bailey type, introduced to England shortly before the Norman Conquest and widespread in the century that followed. It multiplied above all in the reign of Stephen, with the so-called 'adulterine' castles, some of which have been revealed for the first time by views from the air. When these castles were razed or decayed, only the mound remained. One such site, unrecorded in print or on any map, is probably revealed by a photograph taken in 1963 of a site near the ancient road known as the Ryknield Street between Alcester and Wixford. This type of castle was rapidly overtaken by the stone keep enclosed by a defensive wall, and this again by the perfect type of fortress-castle evolved by the crusaders in such masterpieces as Crac des Chevaliers, carried back to France in such edifices as Château Gaillard, and

perfected in its classic expression by the engineers of Edward I. The string of massive fortresses imposed upon the Welsh landscape after the Edwardian conquest, along the northern coast from Chester to Beaumaris, by Harlech (Plate 65) to Pembroke and the marches of Monmouth and Herefordshire, is without peer in any country of Europe. Here the air photograph can show at a glance, as with the monastic ruin, the elaborate plan with its defences, curtain walls, masked entrances and concentric approaches and towers, while oblique views of Harlech or Carreg Cennen show the skill and purpose of the architects in the matter of siting. A photograph from the air can show the development of the later domesticated Compton Wynyates or Baddesley Clinton (Warwickshire) from the island-castles such as Bodiam or Herstmonceaux (Sussex).

With a series of photographs it is possible to trace what has been called the 'dissolution of the medieval landscape'.[11] Those of Laxton and Braunton (Devon)[12] show the open fields, no longer indeed split up into a multitude of strips but still, even after the consolidation of holdings, giving the unwary at first sight the impression of looking at the display of a nurseryman or a bulb-grower rather than at a variety of cereals and roots. At Middleton-in-Pickering (Yorkshire, N.R.) early enclosure 'fossilized' the strips with hedges that have since delimited the narrow fields of an ordinary farm.[13] At Padbury, as we have seen (Plate 63), the hedges of the enclosure radiate from the village across the grain of the furrows of the medieval fields.

Air photography, as is well known, was used in World War II on a vast scale in the preparations for air attack and to record the results of bombing. It combines the data of a photograph and of a plan; in addition, it often shows the historian at a glance the extent of the original medieval city or village, and of the various additions or shrinkages that have taken place. Thus a photograph of Milan shows the line of fortifications of the late medieval and early modern city, while one of Gothenburg shows the extent of the seventeenth-century port and mart. A group of frontier towns and cities on the northern boundary of the France of Louis XIV show to perfection the principles of the French king's great engineers, who set the fashion for Europe in competition

Plate 65. Harlech Castle, Merionethshire (SH581313)—a castle built by Edward I. The photograph shows both the castle plan with its bastions and elaborate gate-house, and the site, perched upon precipitous crags.
BP 53   *20 July 1948*

Plate 65.   Harlech Castle

with those of the United Provinces. In England, views of York and Chester[14] show both the extent of the Roman fortress and of the late medieval walls, while at Berwick[15] the medieval wall can be seen enclosing a circuit considerably larger than that of the Elizabethan ramparts. York and other cities show also very vividly the maze of crooked streets that debouched upon the cathedral close.

Everyone is aware that the Romans, when planning a town, favoured the square or at least the quadrilateral shape, with numerous streets intersecting at right angles between blocks or rows of shops and houses. Such a plan could easily include the substitution of an open forum or a group of public buildings for one or more of the 'islands' between the roads. Medieval town-planning is less familiar, and visitors at ground level in the City of London or in York would think it a contradiction in terms. Nevertheless, there are in this country several examples of planned towns, which are seen to the best advantage from the air. Planning could take place only on a virgin site or a conquered place that called for drastic rebuilding. The textbook example is Winchelsea at the extreme of East Sussex. Though now left high and dry some two miles from the sea, it was created by Edward I *circa* 1280 as a port to replace Old Winchelsea which had undergone rapid erosion in the mid-thirteenth century, and it was designed and built on the virgin site of a grassy plateau to the west of the estuary that was later to be silted up. An air photograph shows part of the grid of rectangular street-lines originally enclosing some thirty-nine 'quarters' mostly occupied by houses with their crofts, but without any exit to the fields.[16] Besides Winchelsea Edward I planned or reconstructed a series of towns in North Wales, of which Flint is the most symmetrical,[17] and a number of Newtowns or Newmarkets or Newports were in origin 'planned', often by the founding lord or bishop, and can be recognised as such from the air.

Often an air photograph illustrates a long series of changes. Alcester, a small Warwickshire town on the western border of the county, is a descendant of the Roman settlement at the confluence of the rivers Arrow and Alne, and was from the twelfth to the mid-nineteenth century a busy market town and distributing centre for crafts of various kinds. Ultimately eclipsed by the growth of Birmingham, twenty miles away, it has now lost the two railways that at one time served its needs and trade, and its High Street stands somewhat aloof from the two main roads that now carry long-distance traffic (Plates 66, 67). The main street, with its church and churchyard and town hall on island sites, may have formed originally a section of the Romano-Saxon road running down the Arrow valley. After leaving the town to the south,

by what is now a *cul-de-sac* bordering the site of the Roman cemetery, it crossed the Arrow at a ford near the medieval Oversley mill and later passed through the Avon at Bidford on its way to the Cotswold plateau. The site of the original mill at Alcester itself is preserved by the narrow Mill Lane, containing the town's oldest houses, which runs down to the river opposite the church. The houses of the main street, the modern High Street and Henley Street, can be seen from the air with their medieval crofts, now partly occupied by sheds and small workshops, terminated by the service lane that is a common feature of the English village plan. Beyond the lane in earlier times ran a stream that may have represented the original course of the Arrow. In a memorable flood in January 1900, the present river made a temporary 'cut-off' by this route, flooding the foot of High Street and carrying merchandise across the fields to rejoin the main stream south of the town. At some time in the medieval period the road system changed its character. Henley-in-Arden to the north-east, Evesham to the south and Stratford-on-Avon to the south-east became focal points. The ford on the Roman road was abandoned and overlaid with a mill-pond, bridges were built on the Stratford and Henley roads, and the Evesham road, turning westwards out of the town, took its course over high ground after leaving the valley beyond the hamlet of Arrow to run through what later became the enclosed park of Ragley Hall. To the north, in more recent times, the pull of Birmingham deflected the course of the old road and gave importance to its exit from Alcester. It does not touch the High Street and had few houses along its sides before it became the approach to the railway station in the 1860s. Meanwhile there is some evidence that the old market-place near the main cross-roads was built over, and the market transferred to the broad Henley Street around the Town Hall. Thus in the early modern period only one of the four main roads converging on Alcester passed through the market and High Street. The recent accretions at the perimeter are clearly visible in the photograph, with the line of railway, itself now an antiquity, beyond.

In the open country, also, an air photograph can show eventful changes. A view of Harewood (Yorkshire W.R.) shows how in the mid-eighteenth century a landowner could move a village, divert a turnpike road and replant his tenants in a 'model' village at his lodge gates.[18] At Harewood, when the park had been enclosed, the church was left standing alone not far from the new mansion, while the road running through the village was diverted, and the householders moved outside the enclosure into a housing estate devised to provide an expanding

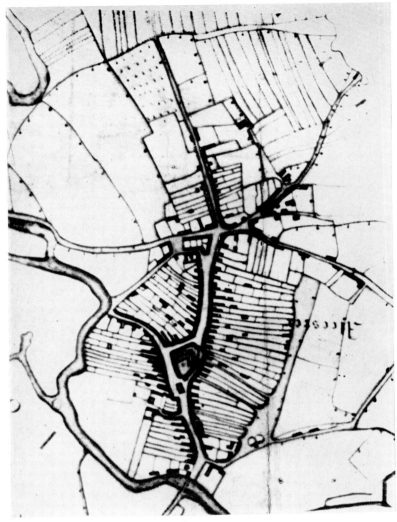

Plate 66.   Alcester

Plate 66.   Alcester, in 1752. The plan should be compared with the air photograph (Plate 67), which has the same orientation.
(*Birmingham Reference Library, MSS. 379051*)

Plate 67.   Alcester, Warwickshire (SP089573). The view is to the south.
WO 59   *24 June 1958*

Plate 67.   Alcester, looking south

Plate 68. Wimpole Hall, Cambridgeshire (TL 335510), looking south. Several of the leading eighteenth-century landscape gardeners had a hand in laying out the grounds of Wimpole, but it is the work of 'Capability Brown' that mainly survives. The photograph shows the boldness of these men in creating great sweeps of park-land, the double avenue of trees forming a vista of more than two miles from the house.
ER 64   28 July 1949

Plate 68.   Landscape gardening

vista of the main entrance to the park. At Milton Abbas (Dorset) a small market town was extinguished by purchase and the rare inhabitants who clung to the land were housed in a much smaller 'garden village' out of sight of the landowner's windows.[19]

In addition to, or in combination with, such transferences of population the rural landscape of England in the mid-eighteenth century underwent a revolution comparable in scale to the industrial revolution that brought about a shift of population towards the new mines and mills of the north and north midlands. The widespread enclosures replaced the open fields with areas bounded by quickset hedges along which lofty trees were planted at intervals to give shade to the cattle. In almost every large parish a mansion with spreading gardens appeared, and the larger members of the species, of which the apex was formed by palaces such as Blenheim, Castle Howard or Wilton, were surrounded by wide tracts of well wooded parkland with avenues and lakes imposed upon the quilt-like pattern of ploughed fields or meadows. The social and administrative life in these mansions, inhabited by the lords of wide acres, their guests and their myriad retainers, remained almost intact till 1914, and is still prolonged here and there on a greatly reduced scale. An air view can show as no other the splendours of a vanished age. Wimpole Hall, a few miles south-west of Cambridge, was begun on a modest scale in 1632 and vastly extended in the eighteenth century by Edward Harley, Earl of Oxford and Charles Yorke, Earl of Hardwicke. The surroundings were landscaped by Capability Brown between 1767 and 1773 and by Repton in 1801. The photograph (Plate 68) shows the southern half of the park cut out of the rural pattern of Cambridgeshire, with the trees spaced to give a 'pleasing prospect'. A sham ruin, some half-mile from the house, gave interest to the view from the windows. The avenue runs down to the Old North Road (Ermine Street, now A14), the line of which can be seen forming an acute angle with the right-hand line of trees. Another ancient road, the Akeman Street, crosses the avenue at the third line of bushes, and the infant Cam a little further down. Air photographs of the park to the north of the house show the site of the old village surrounded by the ridge-and-furrow of its open fields. The village New Wimpole is off the plate to the left.

The plate of Wimpole reminds us that an air photograph can give new dimensions to a map by showing a Roman road striding across hill and dale. It can now show also the deficiencies of the first hastily-planned railways, avoiding for some accidental reason a centre of population, as the old Birmingham-Bristol line by-passes Worcester, and the main London-Crewe main line avoids Northampton. In a very few years it will serve to show the lines of an outmoded system of communications, surviving only in what have proved to be the most permanent of all human works, the cutting or the embankment.

NOTES

[1] For a sketch plan of Yeavering see H. M. Colvin, in *The History of the King's Works* (H.M.S.O., 1963), I, 3. A detailed report of the excavations is to follow.

[2] M. W. Beresford and J. K. S. St Joseph, *Medieval England, an Aerial Survey* (Cambridge, 1958), 42.

[3] *Medieval England*, 26-9.

[4] *Medieval England*, 112-14.

[5] D. Knowles and J. K. S. St Joseph, *Monastic Sites from the Air* (Cambridge, 1952), 78-81.

[6] *Monastic Sites*, 160-3.

[7] *Monastic Sites*, 204-5.

[8] *Monastic Sites*, 126-9.

[9] *Monastic Sites*, 134-5.

[10] *Monastic Sites*, 242-5.

[11] *Medieval England*, 109.

[12] *Medieval England*, 42-9.

[13] *Medieval England*, 121.

[14] *Medieval England*, 158, 173.

[15] *Medieval England*, 178-9.

[16] *Medieval England*, 222.

[17] *Medieval England*, 216.

[18] *Medieval England*, 61.

[19] *Monastic Sites*, 34-5.

SIR IAN RICHMOND

Towns and Monumental Buildings

IN this day and generation it is almost a truism to say that the viewpoint of the air photographer has its own particular virtue. The reasons why this should be and the conditions under which the most advantageous pictures can be taken have also been frequently described, if not so widely absorbed. Among subjects, however, towns and great monumental buildings have their own characteristics and the advantages inherent in the application to them of air photography are correspondingly particular in kind. Subjects of this sort are in no sense new discoveries: they are normally well known and their historical significance is usually well appreciated. The value of the air photograph thus consists in offering a new point of view, from which can be obtained a conspectus of innumerable details presented in a unified perspective not attained in normal circumstances by any photograph taken on the ground.

These general results emerge very clearly in a view of the historic stronghold of Shrewsbury, in Shropshire (Plate 69), the key to the medieval Middle March against Wales and the base from which the very heart of Welsh territory could be penetrated by way of the Upper Severn valley. Cartography will, indeed, convey very well the great loop of the river containing the town and its Norman castle, which seizes and occupies the hillock within the loop, making of it first a stronghold and then a bridgehead for movement either into Wales or along the borderland to north or south. Mapping, too, will demonstrate how the railway, spanning the neck of the peninsula, in due course met the same requirements of movement in terms of peaceful communication. But no map can even begin to impart the subtler relationships which give the town its character. First is perceived the river in its flood-plain, above which the fortress and town must rise, then the constriction exercised by its great meander, and the elegant fashion in which man has tamed the encroaching current by reinforcing the town-ward bank with fine trees in a stately variation. Next appear the relation to the crowded town of

the market-places for man and beast, the architectural domination of the town-heads by churches and the freqent usurpation of the ancient house-plots by commercial buildings. It becomes evident how precarious is the hold on the plateau of the two buildings, hospital and prison, for the physically and psychologically sick, now no longer subject to the out-of-date social factors which once exerted a necessarily centripetal attraction. Beyond the river the famous public school and the suburbs impress upon the scene their solutions of other hardly less recent social problems; while below the neck the industrial agglomeration emphasises what the coming of the railway meant to the manufacturer. The practical and theoretical aspects of all such factors and problems in a long history and in multifarious planning are rendered incalculably easier to approach and to appreciate through air photography. This is, moreover, a field in which the oblique photograph is superior to the vertical, for it arranges the points in more significant perspective, both literally and metaphorically.

More restricted but no less interesting problems of historic and urban development are suggested at Caernarvon (Plate 70), where a trim Welsh borough, founded and shaped by King Edward I in 1284 to be the capital of the principality of North Wales, lies engulfed yet isolated in the modern town. The forecourt of the noble castle occupies the site of the Norman motte of 1090; its rearcourt and huge residential towers, dominated by the three seaward look-out turrets on the biggest tower of all, control the river-harbour of the Seiont. The sedate market-place outside the Castle gate was once the Norman outer bailey: it is now the modern town-centre, in which the only jarring note is the round feature towards the middle, but a rival place of concourse is the embanked river-quay which covers the ancient strand. Edward's royal borough is still encompassed by its D-shaped defensive wall, within which the original street-plan survives, though rows of modern houses, a market-hall, local government offices, law-courts, prison and

Plate 69.   Shrewsbury, Shropshire, looking south-west (*SJ492123*).   *BL 89   18 July 1948*

Non-conformist chapels have almost obliterated the older buildings. The fourteenth-century chantry chapel of St Mary in the north-west corner, and the modern hall over the East Gate which replaces the Principality's Exchequer, represent the only certain medieval internal buildings. The merging of the ancient land-plots into larger units by sale or inheritance can, however, be clearly detected in the modern house-divisions. Outside the town wall the wide strip on the site of the ancient ditch is once again almost free, thanks to an enlightened policy of clearances. The ancient roads, converging upon the market-place and the Exchequer Gate, have determined the lines of the modern town, here much less haphazard than it might look, though some highly individualistic ribbon-development lies outside the landward limits of the picture. The town-planner will be struck by the contrast between the densely crowded urban area and the gracious amenity of the meadows, woods and shore across the river; while the student of traffic problems will see in this picture, not taken at the height of the holiday season, the threat to amenity presented in the market square by the day-to-day omnibus, and on the strand by the long-distance coaches and private motor-cars. No view at ground-level and no town-plan can convey the scale and relationship of these highly diverse elements. In plan the castle is dwarfed by the ancient town, whereas in elevation it is itself the dominant. Again, the tightly-packed medieval street-system, well conveyed by a plan, cannot on plan be shown in devolution, to the story of which an especially incisive contribution is made by the architectural types of the buildings. Finally, the space-volume relationship of streets and houses to the parked traffic units is particularly well conveyed, with adverse augury for the future.

A completely different aspect of medievalism is presented by the remote cathedral city of St David's, in Pembrokeshire (Plate 71), founded in the earliest days of Welsh Christianity. This 'lighted candle' was deliberately put by St David in 'a secret place', since he chose as his site a secluded glen, which supplied three important needs, namely, a water-supply, a position not obvious to sea-raiders and a solitude appropriate to early monastic life. It compares well with St Deiniol's site at Bangor, which, however, is much more heavily overlaid by modern buildings. At St. David's the primitive monastery buildings, no doubt as devoid of architectural pretension as those of any other Celtic foundations, were long ago superseded by a great Norman cathedral and bishop's palace, not to mention a subordinate church, all enclosed by a great walled precinct, entered through a massive towered gate-house at the top of the slope. The township, as small a cathedral city

as the North Welsh St Asaph, is elbowed on to the surrounding plateau. Here lies the market-place, at the junction of three approach-roads bordered by irregular garden-plots and houses of unambitious harmony, broken only by a garish Nonconformist chapel which turns its back upon the episcopal domain.

The vast cathedral, a pilgrimage church of great fame, bestrides a little coomb in the valley side and runs down its length, dropping in level from east to west. The site is so low that the great central tower does not rise above the gate-towers of the precinct, and the building makes its impact by surprise as well as by an intrinsic beauty. Decorated windows endow it with lightness as well as scale, in striking comparison with the late Romanesque architecture of the ancient Bishop's hall and church, which are ranged about a great quadrangle; the hall on the east, distinguished by its chequered masonry and machicolated eaves, and the church on the south, with a magnificent arcaded east façade. Alongside the cathedral lies the fourteenth-century collegiate church, of modest and dignified aspect befitting its ancillary function.

The outstanding general impression made upon the beholder at St David's thus derives from the aesthetic relationship of its varied buildings, which is not to be represented by either a comprehensive plan or elevations of the individual units. Only air photography will espy it. But in so doing, it will also record the imaginative and powerful aggrandisement of a Dark Age site at Norman hands, the intricate relation between a monastic cathedral and the adjacent bishop's establishment, and the successive eastward extensions of the great church as the Norman plan, of enhancing the attraction of the holy place to pilgrims, came to fruition. Finally, it will record the development of the little market-town outside the cathedral precinct, the impact of sectarianism upon it and its latter-day choice of a 'beauty of holiness' completely divorced from external grace.

The richness and dignified beauty of later Norman or Plantagenet architecture began to blossom early, but fruited late. What Caernarvon might have looked like in the twelfth rather than the thirteenth century is well shown by the Norfolk earthworks of Castle Acre (Plate 72). Here the massive mounds and ditches of a great motte, an outer bailey and an attached borough still dominate the scene and harbour the village which has taken their place. On the ground, in the wide, flat valley of the Nar, no conspectus of the works can be obtained, and the buildings of the village inevitably obtrude upon any kind of general view. In an air photograph the hamlet takes its place in the background, while the earthworks, accentuated by the trees and bushes which clothe them, become

Plate 70. Caernarvon, a town created by Edward I (*SH478626*). *BP 86 20 July 1948*

Plate 71.   St David's, Pembrokeshire, looking north-west (*SM754254*).   *TF 93   13 June 1956*

Plate 72.   Castle Acre, Norfolk, looking north-west (*TF818152*).   *FX 5   18 June 1951*

Plate 73. Cowbridge, Glamorgan, looking north-west (*SS997746*). *XW 77   19 April 1959*

Plate 74.   Fochabers, Elgin, looking north-west (*NJ345587*).   *GQ 52   14 July 1951*

the dominant pattern. In the middle of the bailey a line of massive foundations provides evidence for internal buildings of masonry, and the masonry defences of the developed castle crown the spreading earthworks with walls and foundations which in their turn fall into a pattern of narrower lines appreciable only from an altitude. A plan will indeed define such lines, but it can hardly evoke the subtleties of relief which convey the three-dimensional relationship between them.

The complete domination and ultimate submergence of an early borough, by the line of communication passing through it, is exemplified by Cowbridge, in Glamorganshire (Plate 73). The place extends along a gentle ridge between streams, the crest crowned by the busy traffic which now disrupts rather than unites the community. The result is reflected in ribbon development, which, in an effort to disengage from the main road, is diverted into minor side-roads. In the foreground, to left of the road, is seen a more recent attempt to create secluded units in the form of closes, while to right there is a zone of factories. The ancient borough, rectangular in plan, occupies the middle background, and a distant corner of its surrounding earthwork emerges to right of the sports field. The position of its ancient nearer gate is shown by a marked roll in the road where it crosses the earthwork. On leaving the town the road continues straight for a short distance and then swerves sharply to secure a stream crossing; and selection of a bridging point also accounts for the similar swerve and sharp bend in the foreground. The crisp ribbon-development at both ends of the town is evidently related to exploitation of ancient strips or messuages on either side of the road, which may be presumed to have been originally town-lands devoted to cultivation. The closely-packed buildings along the through road and the largely haphazard spread of buildings behind the road frontage have virtually eclipsed the lines of the ancient borough. But it can at once be observed how the air photograph gives the fullest value to the building pattern, by pinpointing the features on the ground and by relating them to contours so gentle as to convey very little in terms of lines on a map. Nor is the presentation of the character of the buildings themselves of any less value than in considering monumental architecture. Each type has its message to convey in terms of social history.

Striking evidence of planned social development is furnished by the new towns created in eighteenth-century Scotland. The neat rectangular burgh of Fochabers, near Elgin (Plate 74), was established in 1798, when the old town was razed to make way for the parkland of Gordon Castle. It is bounded by streets as opposed to defences, and evidently originated as twelve oblong plots with a rectangular *piazza* carved out

of the plots and setting off the town's public buildings on one side of it. The rectangular town-plan was later irregularly prolonged at each end in order to accommodate a hotel, the principal school or academy and a limited number of less crowded private houses. Still more erratic development followed on the riverward side of the town, and there was the inevitable ribbon-development along the main approaches. The original planners seem to have aimed at filling the frontages of each rectangle with contiguous houses, leaving space for gardens within, now attested, where they survive, by their trees. But there has been much encroachment upon the internal spaces, some of it plainly due, as in Wales, to the spread of sectarianism. An appreciation of this kind of development is essentially dependent upon viewing as a whole the different types and styles of building in relation to one another, so that a comprehensive assessment of planning development and stylistic criteria can be made rapidly and simultaneously. Only through the medium of air photography is this possible.

Houses of great estate can be viewed from the air with no less advantage. Audley End, in Essex (Plate 75), though now only about one quarter of its original size, still offers a notable prospect of the architecture of the early seventeenth century, when the brave new vision which had so recently and so dramatically encompassed the earth was reflecting itself in the vogue for an expanse of glazed windows, letting in new light and opening up new prospects. The relationship of these vast windows to the fabric is impressively conveyed by the light and shade which defines the frame without the over-emphasis of an elevational drawing and picks out the translucent areas in dark reflection. The backward-looking choice of thick stone mullions at Audley End attests the strength of tradition and contrasts with the thinner wooden window-frames of the eighteenth century which make a new pattern of the glass. The problem of heating the rooms behind such an expanse of glass is emphasised by the clusters of chimneys concentrated over the sides of the principal rooms and diversified by the turrets and belvederes which give the great house its character and supply necessary access to the roofs for repairs and for cleaning of gutters. The eighteenth-century range, added across the top end of the court, serves as a main ground-floor corridor with picture-gallery above, but how ruthlessly it breaks the earlier harmony can be sensed far better through the bird's-eye view than through a plan or elevation, for it combines both of these and adds reality to them as well. The huge principal court, once seen to left of the existing house, has now vanished without trace, as has the east wing which made a closed court of the main block. Even the elaborate

Plate 75. Audley End, Essex, looking north-west (*TL524382*). *CO 44 21 June 1948*

Plate 76. Nottingham University, the main buildings (*SK541380*). *EX 34   4 June 1950*

nineteenth-century garden-beds and paths only peep through the present-day grass-plots in a vague array. The formal Jacobean horticulture has long disappeared and its place is taken by noble trees which still reflect the eighteenth-century arrangement of the park-land.

The assured classicism of the eighteenth century represents the same social *milieu*, but a taste no longer tentative and governed by the hard Palladianism which the soft English light seems at once to demand and to offset. The first new buildings of Nottingham University (Plate 76), created after the First World War, seem at close quarters to epitomise this spirit of academic discipline, as necessary to the architecture of the building as to the training for which it is the centre. As an essay in twentieth-century traditionalism Nottingham is one of the most interesting examples of its style. The monumental façade of the great courtyard building is very wide, even without the two recessed flanking wings; and it is cleverly prevented from spreading by the extra storey, which forms a fenestrated attic above the central pedimental bay, while the central tower, kept well in the background, offers a really powerful focal point. The front wings are matched by less monumentally conceived rearward counterparts, creating two side courts. The problem of accommodating growing numbers of laboratories and class-rooms is temporarily solved by five long lines, discreetly kept low in a background partly screened by trees. By skilful use of the irregular outline of an informal lake, contrasted with a monumental stone-built terrace, the great building is deliberately transformed into an architectural back-cloth to the vista of the Trent valley which it itself enjoys, thus taking its place in that subtle interplay of designed formality and organised wildness which is the secret of the charm exercised by so many British buildings in a country setting. An aerial view conveys the whole essence of this relationship and forces home the lesson that in preserving, as in creating, such sites the building cannot be self-sufficient: it must unite with its wider surroundings of ridge and vale, and blend with its immediate parkland or lawn, and all must grow up and grow together if they are to make the impact intended by their designer.

It is evident, then, that in historic and monumental sites the subject and its content can be seized and appreciated far more comprehensively and in a far more complete vision through the aerial view than through any other medium. The historian will, perhaps, make the first claim upon its use; but in the present age, when the British landscape is changing so rapidly, geographers, and planners in town or countryside, will come close in the order of potential users. The rival claims of land-use jostle one another in the government office and stretch the application of social justice to breaking-point. Our ancient monumental heritage, having escaped the nineteenth-century Industrial Revolution, is in the twentieth threatened by the much more formidable Economic Revolution. The presentation and evaluation of its claims are the factors which may be decisive for the very survival of every disputed item. Air survey is then the most effective means of recording the present state of our urban problems and all the circumstances of a country environment. Cogently and crisply it can illustrate the essential points upon which to evaluate the position, to plan it afresh and to take counsel for the nation.

Plate 77. Cotswold landscape

LORD ESHER

Air Photographs and Contemporary Planning

TO the contemporary planner (to use an unappetising expression which in fact means 'to the person with some responsibility for our future environment') air photography has three basic uses—in his education, in his practice, and as a check on his executed work. In this section I shall be dealing mainly with the second of these uses, because it is the largest and longest. But it must first be noted that the education of planners, which is in a state of ferment and flux even more marked than most fields of education, is nowadays very weak on its historical side. This is partly because of the pressure of other subjects, partly because while there is ample (though always obsolescent) text-book coverage of the *practice* of physical planning, there has been no good comprehensive textbook of its history since Abercrombie's miniature classic—unless of course one is so to describe Lewis Mumford's monumental trilogy, which it was certainly never intended to be. Consequently students have only the vaguest picture of the development of the Roman and Medieval landscape, of the revolutionary effect on the English scene of the Enclosures, of the origins of the village, of the different types of medieval town, or of the processes of growth of the modern one. Such students, in present conditions of acute shortage of trained people, soon find themselves in the offices of a development company or local authority, plotting major surgical operations on the heart of organisms whose anatomy and metabolism they have never studied. This certainly partly explains the sense we all have that something brutal is being done to the texture and grain of our cities and towns.

It is obvious that air photographs could enliven and illuminate such an historical study. It might be though that so much of the world's surface has been worked over, so much destroyed, that no photographs of what exists now could tell us much about the past. We are lucky to live in an age when this is not so. Not only have we the well-known examples of old settlements and cultivation and fortifications 'grinning through' our fields (to use the house-painter's nice phrase); but if we look about the world we can find unspoilt examples to illustrate our own story from the beginnings of civilisation. African cities like Ibadan and Kano, Indian cities like Ahmedabad and Jaipur, not to mention familiar Mediterranean examples like Aigues-Mortes and Avila, are more evocative of our own Middle Ages than anything that survives in this country. In this country nothing larger than a village has survived from any age complete as a fly in amber; most of our material is a complex web of strands from many centuries. Unravelling it is itself educative and surprising.

The simplest and earliest examples of the use of air photographs in teaching the history of our landscape and its settlement are the views of villages and fields collected and annotated by Beresford and St Joseph in their *Medieval England: An Aerial Survey*. The overlaying of one system of land-use by another and the patterns of settlement deriving from different local circumstances are the main lessons here, and are most clearly brought out by diagrams from the same viewpoint as the photograph. But it is tantalising to stop at the Tudors, and the story of the village needs to be carried right through to the present day, as was done (but without the use of air photography) in Thomas Sharp's *Anatomy of the Village*. There is a surprisingly large aggregate of unused or under-used space in the back-lands of our villages, mainly owing to the length of medieval crofts (Plate 78b), which could make a significant contribution to alleviate the housing shortage without going out on to the exposed and much more conspicuous surrounding farm-land (Plate 78a). But most modern architects and planners and all modern engineers and surveyors have utterly lost the free-and-easy

Plate 77. Cotswold landscape; panorama near Bourton on the Hill, Gloucestershire (foreground at SP183318). The countryside the maps cannot convey, in which trees are more important features than buildings.
TO 25   25 *July* 1956

Plate 78a. Brackley (*for explanation see page 154*)

Plate 78b.   Brill

flair which their ancestors possessed for siting and designing new buildings in old villages. Air photographs bring out better than anything the insensitive, mechanical and boring patterns of modern housing estates alongside the 'instinctive' patterns of the past. They also revealingly show the slightly meandering short-cuts obstinately and even destructively taken by human beings when planners try to impose on them some sort of formal layout that only looks neat on paper. All this is highly educative.

The village is part of the man-made landscape, and cannot be isolated from it. Here air photography is even more revealing, because it gives their true importance to trees, which the Ordnance Maps must virtually ignore. One of the first lessons for the planner is that two-dimensionally the hedgerow pattern is the basic component of the English scene (Plate 77), and three-dimensionally the full-grown individual tree or clump is a more important and monumental object in the landscape than any but the largest buildings. It dominates the ordinary house, whether one's viewpoint is alongside, or from a hilltop, or from an aircraft at any altitude. In planning new developments, whatever their scale, one ignores this pattern at one's peril. Of course it has been done, but only with success on a scale which virtually substitutes a new landscape for the old. The first examples are the great sixteenth- and seventeenth-century avenues and French-style formal gardens, as still survive at Windsor, Wimpole, Cirencester, Bramham and elsewhere. At Wimpole (Plate 68) the great avenue is laid across the field pattern like a poker on a carpet, in a manner that was not to be seen again until the coming of the railways and motorways. In the eighteenth century, with the change of taste from formality to the romantic parkscape of William Kent and Capability Brown (Plate 79), the handling of landscape form at least concedes something to existing contours (which it was bound to do if 'natural' lakes were to be formed), but again the utilitarian hedgerow pattern is swept aside, and we get unprecedented

cases, as at Harewood, Milton Abbas or Nuneham Courtnay, of whole villages being removed from the scene of a new parkscape and neatly rebuilt close by. But in all these grandiloquent operations it was trees and not buildings which exercised the designer's imagination, and present-day air photographs show his vision in the final stages of realisation before its inevitable decay or replacement.

When we come, in our historical course, to the growth of the larger towns and cities, the use of air photographs is more supplementary to the use of plans and diagrams. But here also either tool without the other would be worth much less. Maps without photographs lose the third dimension and, again, ignore trees and 'floorscape' generally, which in towns of any beauty are just as important as buildings to the total effect. Photographs, at any rate oblique ones, without maps obscure urban geometry and the precise configuration of outdoor spaces. Therefore to study the story properly the student needs town maps, site plans and vertical as well as oblique air photographs. Thus equipped, he will find the basic structure of some towns much easier to grasp than others. These will probably be either the quadripartite Roman cities like Chichester, Gloucester or Chester, or the spider's web centripetal medieval city focused on castle, bridgehead or market-place (Plate 80), or the Georgian sections of London and Edinburgh, Bath (Plate 81), Bristol, Newcastle and so on. But the simple fact of dating mainly from a single period does not necessarily produce a simple plan, as he will find by looking down on the central areas of the great Victorian cities, which will stagger him by their ingenuity in avoiding clarity, or the interminable suburban expanses of the twentieth century, whose rationale will appear even more incomprehensible.

However, towns mainly associated with a single period are the exception. In the great majority of cases the centuries both overlie one another, as at York, Bristol or Norwich, and succeed one another in fairly distinct rings as one travels outward from the centre, as most obviously in London, but indeed almost everywhere. This is the European norm, and this is the process the planning student must understand in all its complexity. Fortunately for the analyst, the succeeding fashions in building and planning have always been virtually nationwide,

---

Plate 78a. Brackley, Northamptonshire (SP585370). A linear village with deep crofts and back-land used for housing (left) and playing fields (right).
R.A.F./B/63. *Vertical photograph; scale 1 : 3,000*   29 *June* 1950

Plate 78b. Brill, Buckinghamshire (SP655139). A rambling village at a road junction, with large areas of back-land potentially available for housing. Footpath patterns (top left and lower right) contrast with the regular curves of roads.
R.A.F./B/11. *Vertical photograph; scale 1 : 2,650*   29 *June* 1950

Plate 79. Blenheim, Oxfordshire (SP441161), looking north-west. The formality of Vanbrugh's avenue contrasts with the free sweeping curves of Brown's lake and tree-clumps, showing in one view the two styles of English landscape design.
AN 88   16 *June* 1948

Plate 79.   Blenheim Palace

at any rate south of the Border, so that a set of about a dozen well-chosen subjects should give him the complete story. The Roman cross-roads, the Roman or medieval wall, the Cathedral in its green quadrant the medieval street-grid with its market-place—all these will be found in a single photograph, but the student will note the more recent over-building on what were originally crofts and gardens, the erosion of quirks and bottlenecks, the breaches in walls, the embankment of rivers. Another picture will show the first, and probably still medieval, ribbon-development along the highways, often coalescing with adjoining villages, and the gradually more intense colonisation of the productive hinter-land. Another will show the orderly Georgian and early Victorian accretions, with their terraces, squares, crescents, and later romantic villas embowered in vegetation. Then the surgical cut of the first railway, clumsy or ingenious in the individual case. A set of three or four photographs will illustrate piecemeal industrialisation, small-scale in one city, wholesale in another, the sprawl of goods-yards and sidings, the little black slum terraces jammed in between the factories and rail-ways (Plate 82), then the far more extensive red or grey acres of deadly monotonous bye-law housing in mechanical rows, broken here and there by a Victorian park or cemetery (Plate 83). Further views would show twentieth-century Suburbia, in a New Town or elsewhere (Plate 84), second-growth multi-storey housing in the L.C.C. or Coventry or Sheffield or Glasgow manner, or the new scale and elegant curves of the motorway age, destructive and at the same time creative like so many of the innovations of the past.

Which brings us to the use of air photography in the contemporary day-to-day practice of the architect/planner. Here we must begin with a distinction familiar to him, between Survey and Plan. An immense amount of survey material of many specialised kinds can of course be built up by air photography, including the contoured maps and de-mountable working models, which most urban planners use as the basis for their work. Here I am concerned not with the techniques of aerial survey and mapping, vitally useful though these are to the planner, but with the uses he makes of air photographs themselves. I suggest that these uses, which we must regard as distinct from, but complementary to, the uses of maps and models, are fivefold.

I. MOVEMENT

Expertly interpreted air photographs, mainly enlarged verticals, have the unique advantage of revealing how people move about a landscape or townscape, whether on foot or on wheels. Large numbers of pedestrians, given freedom of movement in limited areas, as at Box Hill in Surrey or Carnac in Brittany, will produce vein-like patterns not unlike the drainage channels in a salt marsh or uncultivated desert. These organic patterns are at the opposite extreme from the geometrical and generally rectilinear patterns that result from the use of drawing instruments and of rectangular building components. This is a functional conflict which Le Corbusier, in his early idealisation of the Cartesian right-angle, disingenuously ignored. Of course, as soon as the planner gets to work on a virgin landscape, even at the elementary stage of parcelling and fencing, free movement is checked and distorted by barriers or attracted to points of concentration, and a new hybrid circulation pattern emerges, in which necessity and choice co-exist in different proportions. This is the kind of pattern we find in a blitzed city: surviving buildings produce points of concentration, but chain-link fences will need to be kept in good repair if every kind of short cut across blitzed sites is not to be taken. The planner will note all these short cuts with care, and if they reflect a layout of public or popular buildings which he intends to retain, he will retain them too, or divert them as little as he can. He will thus be given a clue to the pedestrian, as distinct from vehicular, circulation system he ought to adopt. Its linear forms will tend to be slightly wavy but non-geometrical, hugging all external angles, with a variety of radials from fixed points and a general absence of parallel lines.

Motor vehicle patterns are quite different. Left free, as on a beach or at a race meeting, vehicles will trace interlocking regular arcs in turning, but will head pretty straight from point to point. The engineer knows all this, and provides for the vehicle's special characteristics with more science than he uses in providing for pedestrians. But even here pretty patterns and symmetry are liable to override functionalism, as one can see by observing in air photographs the actual tracks worn by vehicles in passing through a roundabout. One can also learn a great deal about the details of infestation of a town centre by parked cars from a vertical photograph which shows up every ingenious hideout.

2. VEGETATION AND SURFACE CHARACTER

The geographer and the regional planner, particularly in under-developed areas, will obviously obtain a great deal of information on

Plate 80. Norwich (TG231086). The medieval jumble, with motor-car infestation clearly shown.
V-CQ 8. Vertical photograph; scale 1 : 4,050   *29 June 1964*

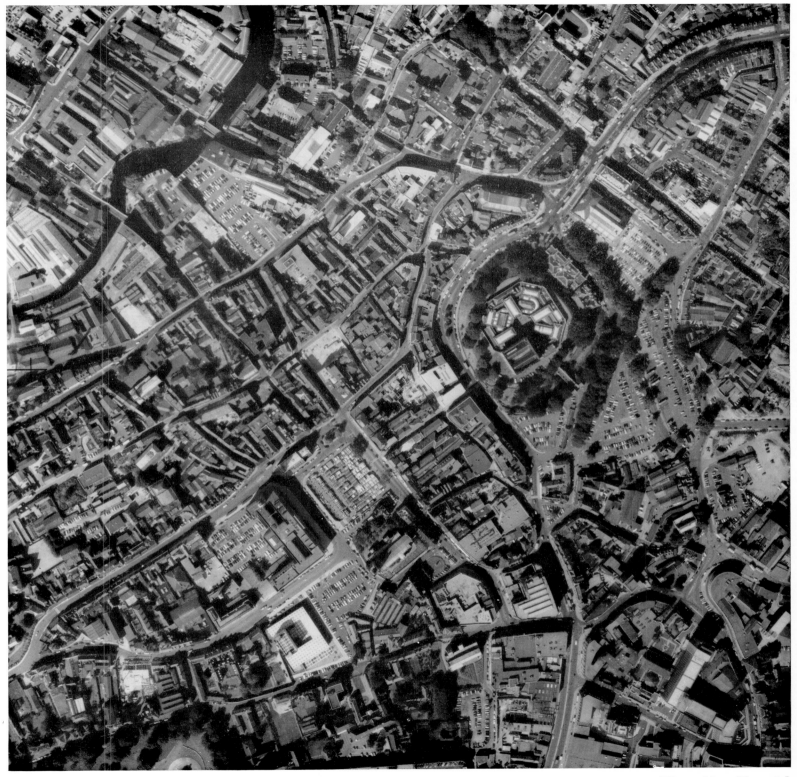

Plate 80.   Norwich

Plate 81.   Bath

Plate 81.   Bath (ST750650), looking north-east. The brief age of urban order, with the landscape brought into the city and buildings unified by the use of a single material.
TL 28   22 July 1956

Plate 82. Longton, Staffordshire (SJ915431), looking north-west. Victorian dereliction, ripe for renewal.
ABA 24   14 June 1960

Plate 82.   Longton

these subjects from air photography, but I am here mainly concerned with the use of air photographs in smaller-scale redevelopment within Britain. Here air photographs have two special uses, both time-saving. One is in giving an immediate and vivid picture of industrial dereliction, old pit-workings etc. in areas available for rehabilitation and redevelopment. The other is in conveying the character and distribution of trees and other vegetation in heavily wooded areas where ground survey would be far more expensive, slow or impracticable. These two types of development area will both incidentally be increasingly important as the growth of population and living standards force us to look for sites which are either already spoiled or well camouflaged, rather than the open farmland where development is too easy and visually damaging. In both cases photographs will need to be supplemented by ground information.

3. SCALE

When an architect speaks of scale he does not mean size. Size is a merely dimensional term, without relativity, whereas scale means size in relation to a fixed unit: the height of a man. Thus a building can be merely big if it consists of a lot of small units on top of one another as in a block of flats; but if a building of the same size contains one unit, one storey, only, like a cathedral or a power station, its scale as well as its size is immense. Scale is therefore one of the attributes of buildings that can be manipulated to produce a deliberate effect, or can be lost sight of with disastrous or absurd results. In most English towns, and of course pre-eminently in the cathedral cities, the house of God was deliberately given a superhuman scale, and its symbolic predominance has become traditional—so traditional in fact that in the larger cities where utilities like power stations and gasholders are in fact the dominating elements, we have learnt the knack of not seeing them: we still like to think of our town silhouettes as an irregular serrated outline broken only by towers and spires.

Air photographs, particularly low-level obliques, at once show up the true state of affairs. The town's great buildings dominate the scene, or if they do not we can see why. We can see the value of intricate small-scale buildings and spaces in setting them off, and if such buildings have to disappear, which in central areas is often the case, we can try out new proposals quickly and simply by superimposing them on the photograph.

4. GRAIN

Such bird's eye views of the intricacies of towns reveal much more than the relativities of scale. They reveal in townscape a texture and directional emphasis as in a woven material or a rough piece of wood. For this most indefinable but most essential characteristic of the fabric of towns architects have recently coined the word 'grain', because 'going against the grain' is a handy way of conveying its converse. Obviously the grain of towns as we have them is not always pleasant. We have acres of Victorian bye-law streets and miles of inter-war speculators' estates whose patterns are either so mechanical or so senseless that their study reveals nothing at all. On the other hand we have in our best cities, towns and villages, from the centre of Manchester down to the smallest Yorkshire hamlet, a grain or theme or texture, call it what you like, which must be discerned if the planner is not to commit every kind of solecism. Air photographs are an indispensable visual aid to this discernment.

5. SYNOPTIC VISION

In analysing the uses of air photography in the teaching and practice of physical planning one inevitably puts the parts before the whole. But the whole is more important than the sum of the parts. It was significant that Sir Patrick Geddes, who was the first British writer on city planning to apply scientific method and intuition rather than aesthetic rule of thumb to its study, should have chosen for his home and workplace the Outlook Tower in Edinburgh, an eyrie on the crest of the Old Town with a panoramic view of the whole city. Before the existence of air photography he spoke and wrote of the necessity for what he called the 'synoptic vision' of the problems of physical planning, of the unified study of the impress of human settlement and cultivation on the earth's surface rather than of 'town and country planning' as conventionally defined. From the air, in which administrative and national demarcation lines are invisible and meaningless, and the distinction between town and country is blurred, we have no alternative to a sense of proportion. The practising planner who has not seen his problem from the air, and who is not, on any commercial flight, among the first in the race for a window seat, can only be falling down on his job.

It follows that we have in air photography not merely a tool of our trade, but a test of our achievement. Where, as in the Black Country or

Plate 83. York, housing estates to south of the medieval city (SE607508). Late Victorian bye-law housing estates and inter-war speculative 'semis' round the cemetery—the negation of planning. O 53. Vertical photograph; scale 1 : 3,850   28 July 1948

Plate 83. York

Plate 84. Housing estates, Oscott

the South Lancashire conurbation or even, on a mercifully smaller scale, in the recent rebuilding of the City of London, we have made a mess of our environment air photography takes the lid off it. Where a new order is beginning to emerge, as in some of the latest work of the L.C.C., of Sheffield, Coventry, Glasgow, of the most recent New Towns, air photography dramatises it. One qualification only must be made. We do not live in aircraft, and the view they give us is not the final test. The final test of an environment for 'liveability' is by living in it. Air photography, which makes almost any pattern look pretty and tidies away the junk-yard, the pylon and the whole foreground paraphernalia that by the laws of optics dominate any earthbound scene, would be a snare and a delusion if it released us for one moment from this ultimate responsibility.

Plate 84. Oscott, north of Birmingham (SP081943), looking north-west. Local authority low-density housing; a pretty pattern from the air, but a heartless desert on the ground.
YP 31   20 June 1959

INDEX

Note. Figures in italic type refer to pages bearing illustrations.

Printed in Great Britain at the Aberdeen University Press